THE STORY OF BRIDGES

ARCHIBALD BLACK

READERS of all ages will be fascinated by this story of bridges and bridge building from the first primitive log and vine structures down to the latest miracles of engineering skill. All types of bridges are discussed, and the author not only tells how they are built but some of the thrilling stories of their builders, their successes and their failures. Perhaps no branch of engineering is more filled with romance—from the Roman pontoon bridges which were opened with human sacrifice, and the castle bridges and covered bridges of the middle ages, to the first ambitious metal bridges (when engineers still used the trial-and-error method), and the tremendous spans of today. Special attention is given to bridges illustrating unusual engineering problems, and outstanding modern structures such as the George Washington Bridge and the two new San Francisco bridges.

The sixty-six remarkable photographs used as illustrations have been collected from all over the world.

Archibald Black is a special writer for the Port of New York Authority, and is the author of *Transport Aviation* and *Civil Airports and Airways*.

Frontispiece.—This George Washington Bridge tower becomes a study in steel.

THE
STORY OF BRIDGES

BY
ARCHIBALD BLACK

New York **WHITTLESEY HOUSE** *London*
McGRAW-HILL BOOK COMPANY, INC.

FIRST EDITION

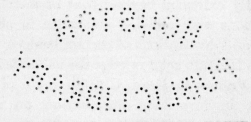
PUBLISHED BY WHITTLESEY HOUSE
A division of the McGraw-Hill Book Company, Inc.

Printed in the United States of America by The Maple Press Co., York, Pa.

Preface

THIS book takes the form of an illustrated story featuring the romance of bridge building and written entirely for the lay reader. No effort has been made to cover the more technical aspects of bridge building and, for obvious reasons, the account has been limited to bridges which are more than purely local in their interest. The greatest possible care has been given to checking the accuracy of all figures and dates, but surprising discrepancies were found to exist between various sources of information. In all these cases, the figures regarded as most reliable were taken.

The author finds it difficult to express fully his appreciation of the very generous cooperation rendered by those individuals and organizations mentioned in the accompanying list of acknowledgments. Their aid frequently extended beyond that of merely supplying illustrations and included assistance in obtaining the history and descriptions of certain bridges. This opportunity is taken to acknowledge the valuable aid rendered by Mr. Francis C. Read, City Surveyor of the City of London, in furnishing information on old London bridges.

To Dr. David B. Steinman of the firm of Robinson and Steinman, designers of the Mount Hope, St. Johns,

v

Waldo-Hancock and numerous other bridges, and to Mr. Allston Dana, formerly Engineer of Design for the Port of New York Authority on the Bayonne, George Washington, and other bridges and later Engineer of Design for the Triborough Bridge Authority, the author is particularly indebted for their assistance in commenting upon and correcting the text. Thanks are also due to Mr. William F. Gould, Assistant Engineer, Port of New York Authority, and to Mr. M. C. Kupfer, Assistant Engineer, Triborough Bridge Authority, for similar aid.

ARCHIBALD BLACK.

GARDEN CITY, N.Y.,
August, 1936.

Acknowledgments

ACKNOWLEDGMENT is due to each of the following for the use of photographs and descriptions of bridges: Aluminum Company of America; American Bridge Company; Ash-Howard-Needles and Tammen; Associated British Railways, Inc.; Baltimore and Ohio Railroad Company; California Toll Bridge Authority; California Department of Public Works; Canadian National Railways; Chicago and Alton Railroad; City of New York, Department of Parks; City of New York, Department of Plant and Structures; Committee on Public Relations of the Eastern Railroads; County of Allegheny, Department of Highways, Bridges and Tunnels; Danish State Railways; Delaware, Lackawanna and Western Railroad Company; Delaware River Joint Commission of Pennsylvania and New Jersey; Dorman, Long and Company, Ltd.; Engineering News-Record; "ENIT," Ente Nazionale Industrie Turistiche (Italy); Florida East Coast Railway Company; Ford, Bacon and Davis, Inc.; German Railroads Information Office, New York; Golden Gate Bridge and Highway District; Indian Government Railways (including Assam-Bengal Railway Company, Ltd., Bengal-Nagpur Railway Company, Ltd., Bombay, Baroda and Central India Railway Company, Burma Railways, H.E.H.

the Nizam's State Railway, North Western Railway, South Indian Railway Company, Ltd.); Italian Tourist Information Office, New York; Gustav Lindenthal; Long Island State Park Commission; McClintic-Marshall Corporation division of Bethlehem Steel Corporation; Michigan Central Railroad; New Jersey State Highway Commission; New York Central Railroad Company; Norwood-Noonan Company; Parsons, Klapp, Brinckerhoff, and Douglas; Pennsylvania Department of Highways; Pennsylvania Railroad Company; Philadelphia Electric Company; Portland Cement Association; The Port of New York Authority; Railways of France; Francis C. Read, City Surveyor, London; Robinson and Steinman; John A. Roebling's Sons Company; Scandinavian Travel Bureau, New York; Société pour le Développement de Fribourg; Southern Pacific Company; Standard Oil Company of California; Dr. D. B. Steinman; Strauss and Paine, Inc.; Strauss Engineering Corporation; Swiss Federal Railroads; Triborough Bridge Authority; Westchester County Park Commission.

ARCHIBALD BLACK.

GARDEN CITY, N. Y.,
August, 1936.

Contents

CONTENTS

X

CONTENTS

erecting a movable bridge—cantilever construction of vertical lift span —concrete construction.

List of Illustrations

List of Illustrations

xiii

LIST OF ILLUSTRATIONS

LIST OF ILLUSTRATIONS

LIST OF ILLUSTRATIONS

Fig. 1.—Golden Gate Bridge, spanning the entrance to San Francisco Bay.

Fig. 2.—Temporary footwalks link the Golden Gate towers as cable spinning begins.

FIG. 3.—An aerial view of the San Francisco-Oakland Bridge.

The Story of
Bridges

Chapter I

"Big Bridges Are Built under Water"

Two "Biggest" Bridges.

ON THE Pacific Coast a situation has arisen that has had no equal in bridge building. There, within the radius of a few miles in the San Francisco area, are two bridges which have the distinction of holding *a majority* of the world's "big bridge" records. One of these giants, spreading its steel web over the Golden Gate, is a bridge with the longest span ever constructed. Just a few miles away is the stupendous San Francisco-Oakland Bay Bridge, comprising over seven miles of large bridges that together were the biggest bridge-building job in history and made several other size records at the same time. Both bridges brought foundation problems that were equally unprecedented as to size, depth and construction difficulties.

Foundations, it happens, present a problem that began with the earliest of bridges. And, as bridges grew bigger, foundation jobs became still bigger. It wasn't only size; it was the matter of having to put piers out in

3

deeper water and of having to go deeper with their footings. When it came to building these two in California, the engineers had to face some of the greatest foundation problems that bridge builders have yet been called upon to solve. For they had to contend with greater depth as well as greater size and with tides as well as with open sea.

The Greatest Span in the World.

The story of the Golden Gate bridge really began in 1917, when the City Engineer of San Francisco presented this problem to Joseph B. Strauss. At earlier dates there had been some vague dreams of such a bridge, although practical engineers scoffed at them, frowning upon the project as an impossible task and a hopeless venture. The inventive genius of Strauss, a bridge builder of established reputation, had served largely to bring the bascule lift bridge up to its modern, highly efficient state. This, to most men, would have been enough in itself.

But Strauss had other ideas. Anticipating a coming era of great bridges, he had made exhaustive studies of their possibilities and the Golden Gate problem found him prepared. He had no illusions about the size of the job he was picking for himself. It meant the longest span, by a margin that was breath-taking. It meant bridging a gap of more than 4,000 feet—over sixteen city blocks and nearly two and a half times the space crossed by the Quebec Bridge, then the longest span in

4

existence. Nobody had ever considered a span of such unheard-of proportions. Even Lindenthal's daring projects for spanning the Hudson had proposed a bridge of only 3,200 feet and *that* bridge was never built. The George Washington Bridge, with its 3,500-foot span, had not yet been thought of. And, certainly, no engineer had ever proposed putting a bridge pier out in deep sea, as would have to be done to avoid planning a bridge with the almost prohibitive span of more than 5,300 feet!

Strauss's troubles began about the time that he first thought of that bridge, and they've kept him pretty busy since. The first were engineering problems. The matter of spanning the one-mile expanse of water, he decided, could be solved only by putting one of his piers in the water, since his first investigation showed that relatively shallow water covered a rocky ledge extending out more than a thousand feet from the San Francisco side.

"Relatively shallow" it certainly was, for the same investigation showed the ledge to be sixty-five to eighty-five feet below the choppy surface of the water, where a tidal flow had swept the bottom clean right down to the bare rock. Farther out it was even deeper. So the problem boiled down to that of constructing a bridge-pier foundation in eighty-five feet of fairly rough water with tides that left only a couple of hours in each day when divers could work.

It was here that the engineer's imagination got into its stride. Man had already run breakwaters out into the sea to provide safe havens for ships. Why not apply the same principle to this problem? Here, it seemed, was the answer to one difficulty. Strauss would build first a concrete protective fender. Then, in the calm water within, he could follow the conventional practice of bridge builders and sink a steel-box pier caisson through the water down to a solid foundation in the rock. On the face of it, his scheme looked just as simple as that, although Strauss himself had had enough bridge-building experience to expect anything.

So much out of the way, he turned next to the problem of financing. The lowest guess at the cost of bridging the Gate had been $100,000,000; the highest was $220,000,000. In the face of these prohibitive figures, Strauss presented his relatively modest estimate of $27,165,000, for the cost of the bridge, exclusive of administration, financing and similar costs. Even at this, it was obvious that he would have to depend upon public approval. So the next question was that of "selling" his idea to the people of San Francisco.

Here entered another factor, in what certain groups like to call the "vested interests." They had, or thought they had, something to lose by the construction of this bridge. Perhaps to others the plan was just a little too daring. In any case, active opposition arose, making a counter-appeal to the residents, when it became evident that the plan would require their support, for the financing method called for the formation of a body to be known as the "Golden Gate Bridge and Highway District," an organization in the nature of a semipublic body, to be created by several counties in the territory at each end of the bridge. Bonds were to be sold by this body, the interest and amortization to be paid from tolls collected on the bridge.

A whispering campaign of objection began. Voters were misinformed regarding their responsibilities in case the enterprise should become a financial failure. Interests concerned with shipping and military authorities began to worry about the suggestion of bridging the Gate. Feelings ran high and accusations were freely bandied about. A local newspaper fighting for the bridge came out and charged certain interests with using underhanded methods to block the whole scheme, an accusation which was denied promptly and with righteous indignation by the group against which it was aimed.

All of this was still going on when something startling happened on the other side of the continent. The George Washington Bridge over the Hudson, built under the direction of O. H. Ammann, was opened in 1931. The faint sound of the snip of scissors parting a silk ribbon carried nearly 3,000 miles across a continent and brought most unexpected repercussions on its other shore. That part of the opposition which had centered its efforts upon ridiculing the Golden Gate Bridge suddenly found itself metaphorically sitting out on a limb that had just been neatly sawed off the tree! It was one thing to laugh at this 4,200-foot bridge when the longest existing span was only 1,800 feet. Overnight, it became another story, when a 3,500-foot bridge was in actual use; even the most skeptical had to take the Strauss plan seriously. This, with other factors, probably had its influence when the people of San Francisco came to vote on the question in 1932, for the answer was overwhelmingly in favor.

Bombing Out an Excavation under Water.

With *that* problem out of the way, Strauss could turn to those of actual engineering. In October of 1932, a contract for the construction of the main piers was let to the Pacific Bridge Company. On January 5, 1933, work began on the San Francisco and Marin sides of the Gate simultaneously. When a trestle to run 1,125 feet out into the Gate to the site of the San Francisco pier was started, there began a sequence of events that was destined to remove any lingering trace of leisure from the daily routine of all identified with the Golden Gate Bridge.

After several months of hard work and fighting of tides, a steel trestle was finally completed, forming a working platform out to the pier site. At nearly the same moment, a 2,000-ton steamer collided with the new structure 400 feet from the shore, carrying away a substantial part of the platform which had been laboriously constructed. Repairs were made, the gap was bridged with timber to save time, and the work was resumed. Now began the job of excavating rock beneath sixty-five to eighty-five feet of water, with a tidal flow that

8

swept the bottom clean with every movement. The conditions had no parallel in bridge building; but, for that matter, neither had the bridge itself. Some most original methods were needed to make excavations at all possible. Since ordinary blasting operations were entirely out of the question, it was decided to attempt the use of submarine bombs.

Small bombs were used first and with these the bottom rock was loosened to a sufficient depth to make the next step practical. Large bombs that contained 200 pounds of high explosive, each, were then deliberately driven into the loosened bottom with all the force that could be exerted by a 2,500-pound drop hammer! Blasting caps were then attached to the firing device and the explosive detonated. In spite of the apparently tremendous risk in forcibly hammering large bombs into place, the method was eminently successful. No serious accidents occurred. In fact, the scheme proved to be just another one of those ideas that look perfectly crazy until someone finds by experiment that they are thoroughly practical. Each of the series of bombings loosened the rock to a depth of as much as fifteen feet, after which the debris was removed by means of steel-jawed clamshell buckets, lowered and raised by wire ropes. As bomb after bomb was exploded against the rocky bottom, the loosened rock was cleared away and the hole gradually deepened, until a space had been excavated down to the required level.

Section by section the contractor now began install-

9

ing the great forms for the concrete fender. The third section had just been lowered into place and riveted to the others when the elements decided to take part in the game. On October 31, 1933, a severe storm arose. Indeed, it happened to be one of the worst in the history of the locality. Tremendous waves rolled through the Gate and swept the forms out of place as if they were toys. Most of the erection equipment accompanied them.

The workers salvaged what they could, replaced what they couldn't salvage, and started all over again. No sooner was the work resumed than another terrific storm swept through the Gate, rolling up great waves on its way. This time the destruction was considerably more thorough. The waves did not stop at merely wrecking the equipment. They took most of the long trestle at the same time. When the skies cleared again, the builders found that there had been left only 600 feet of their platform. The rest had been completely removed and quite effectively distributed in a tangled mass of steel at the bottom of the water. In December of 1933 a new and stronger trestle was begun and by March of 1934 it was ready. Work was resumed once more and, for a time at least, continued without any further serious disaster.

The Caisson Scheme Is Abandoned.

As we have said, the concrete fender was to serve as protection for the pier during construction. With the enclosure nearing completion, all were beginning to congratulate themselves in the belief that their worst troubles were over.

One side of the concrete oval had been left open to permit floating into place the caisson, a great steel and wood box that was to be sunk down to the rocky bottom and filled with concrete to form the pier itself. In October of 1934, with the aid of tugboats and to the accompaniment of that picturesque language that only seafaring men seem able to attain, this great caisson was finally maneuvered into the shelter of the fender. Everyone began to breathe more freely and the contractor started his preparations to close the gap in the fender wall.

A new and totally unexpected variety of complication now ensued. Another storm favored the toilers with its attention and lashed the waters of the Golden Gate into heavily rolling waves. Through the still-open portion of the fender water began to roll back and forth with a vigor that was most disconcerting to the harrassed engineers. Before anything could be done to prevent it, the heavy caisson became infected with the spirit of the storm and began pounding itself heavily against the fender walls. As the force grew with each thunderous collision, it soon was evident that both caisson and fender were in danger of becoming a total loss. Something had to be done and done quickly. The tugs were recalled and a group of now thoroughly disgusted men fought to remove the damaged caisson just as feverishly as they had fought, only a short time before, to work it into the

11

"protection" of the fender. Some other method of construction would have to be used.

The badly battered box was towed out to sea and sunk, much to the relief of the tugboat crews. Their work was finished, even though it left the foundation problem still unsolved.

Meanwhile, another plan was being put into effect and the open gap in the fender was closed with concrete. While the water still remained inside, several large pipes were sunk down to a resting place upon the rocky bottom. These were, later, to serve as a means of inspecting the rock surface. Once they had been set in position, concrete was "tremied" (placed under water by use of pipes) to the bottom, within the fender and outside of the pipes. After sixty-five feet of depth had been thus filled with concrete, the water remaining above it was pumped out. Each of the big pipes was then capped with an airlock, the water inside was removed and compressed air was applied to prevent more water from leaking in at the bottom. Workers now descended to the bottom of each pipe and cleaned off the rock surface; engineers examined its condition, found this satisfactory, and ordered the pipes filled up with concrete.

Building up the balance of the pier was then resumed. By January of 1935, the last batch of concrete had been poured into place and the pier was up to its finished level, forty-four feet above the waters of the Golden Gate. About this time, Strauss and several of his equally overworked associates began to breathe normally again.

The worst part of their job was over. All that remained was to build a bigger span than had ever been built before. In comparison with fighting the Pacific Ocean, that would be relatively simple.

* * * *

The Biggest Bridge Job in the World.

While Strauss was having his difficulties with that south pier, a group of equally determined engineers was having its own particular brand of trouble a few miles to the east. For here C. H. Purcell and his aids were directing construction of the stupendous San Francisco-Oakland Bay Bridge—from any one of several points of view the biggest bridging enterprise in the world. Not just a single bridge, this is a whole series of great spans, the main structures totaling over five miles, without even counting the elevated approaches and the double-decked tunnel through Goat Island.

This tunnel, in itself, was a record-breaking job; big enough to clear a five-story building, it has the largest bore of any tunnel ever built. The bridge foundations involved both the deepest and the largest underwater foundations ever built; the two suspension spans over the West Bay are exceeded only by the George Washington and Golden Gate bridges and the great East Bay cantilever is exceeded only by those of the Forth and Quebec bridges. The whole project took the greatest tonnage of steel ever used in one job and the engineers estimated that the amount of steel and concrete which

13

they used would have built thirty-five large skyscrapers, while the lumber required for construction purposes would have built 3,000 small homes, or about enough for a town of 15,000 people.

With such quantities of material and so great a structure, it seems only natural to find out that the work required a greater expenditure than any previous bridge. Its total estimated cost is $77,000,000, which compares with the $55,000,000, cost of the George Washington Bridge, $44,200,000, for New York's new Triborough Bridge and $37,000,000, for the Golden Gate Bridge. Even the Florida East Coast Railway's former "railway that went to sea" begins to look almost modest, with its total of $49,000,000.

With the Golden Gate and Bay bridges under construction at the same time, one can picture individual members of the two engineering groups snatching a few hours away from their worries, of an evening, to compare notes or subject each other to friendly "razzing" across the table of some San Francisco café. For Purcell's cohorts, just as truly as Strauss's engineers, had their own problems to face in building the Bay Bridge. Not the least of them was the matter of pier foundations that went down 242 feet below low-water level, or about sixty-five feet farther than the deepest ever built before. This, without even mentioning the rest of their problems in constructing two of the biggest suspension spans, one of the biggest cantilevers and the largest bore tunnel in the world.

14

Now, that 242-foot depth may not be a figure to impress the reader. As a matter of fact, it isn't much of a figure if we're thinking of distance measured along a sidewalk or through some vacant lot. In case your own reaction is somewhat along these lines, stop across the way from a twenty-story building. A look upwards to that cornice high above the sidewalk, marking the edge of the roof, will give a much better illustration of the depth of Purcell's foundations than anything that could possibly be written here. Those 242 feet of water overhead meant a weight of seven and a half tons pressing down upon every square foot at the bottom of the caissons. Naturally, this is far beyond the limit of endurance of compressed-air workers. Few divers can withstand such terrific pressure and those men can stand it for only very short periods at a time. Yet some way had to be found whereby a foundation could be constructed at this unusual depth or the bridge would never rear its proud steel towers high into the heavens. If the science of engineering had been static, perhaps this bridge would never have been built. But out of these problems were born several new ideas in deep-water foundations, including an entirely new kind of compressed-air caisson. That, however, is getting a little ahead of our story.

Some History of Bay Bridge Projects.

The Bay Crossing project has a longer history than the Golden Gate Bridge. No less an authority than Purcell himself credits the first suggestion of bridging the bay to Leland Stanford, that pioneer railroad builder who brought the old Central Pacific Railroad (now part of the Southern Pacific) through to Oakland in 1868, affording the rapidly developing area of San Francisco Bay its first direct rail connection with the East. This was about a year ·before the 1,595-foot Brooklyn Bridge had even been started; John A. Roebling was still wearing out shoe leather in trying to sell his idea to the then separate cities of New York and Brooklyn and the longest span in actual use was his 1,057-foot Ohio River Bridge at Cincinnati.

Looking back at this first bay-crossing project in the light of our knowledge of bridge engineering of those times, one is tempted to question the motives prompting Stanford's project and to wonder if they were entirely free from recognition of its publicity value. Nevertheless, there is some cause to believe that he really thought he could build the bridge, although he never actually tried to do so. After the first flurry of excitement, this original bridge proposal faded into history. But it never was entirely forgotten. Indeed, it continued to keep bobbing up periodically, very much like the proverbial bad penny; and, as the cross-bay ferry traffic grew with the whole area, the recurrent bridge proposals began to assume greater significance with the passing of years.

By 1929, the ferries were carrying, annually, 35,900,000 pedestrians and 4,490,000 vehicles contain-

FIG. 4.—General view of Goat Island during construction of the San Francisco-Oakland Bridge.

FIG. 5.—First floor-truss section being lifted into place, San Francisco-Oakland Bridge.

ing another 10,000,000 persons or more. Something like 50,000 persons living in the territory east of the Bay were traveling daily from their homes to places of employment in San Francisco and returning in the evening. The world-famous Ferry Building tower looked down upon the busiest ferry terminal in the world. Bay-crossing projects were rolling up powerful support among the residents on each side and at one time as many as thirty-five rival groups were jostling elbows in their efforts to obtain the necessary franchises. By this time the advantages of construction as a public enterprise were becoming recognized and in 1929 the state created the California Toll Bridge Authority, with power to build bridges anywhere in the state, financing their construction by the sale of revenue bonds. This body undertook the problem of bridging the bay, assigned the design work to the State Department of Public Works, appointed C. H. Purcell as Chief Engineer of the project and began work.

Purcell, a graduate of the University of Nebraska and for two years a student at Leland Stanford University, had, since 1906, been building bridges for railroads, the Oregon State Highway Department, the U. S. Bureau of Public Roads and the California State Highway Department. He had been a convert to this "bridge-the-bay" idea for many years and in his position as State Highway Engineer he took an active part in some of the engineering investigations that preceded the actual start of work. Hence it seemed that, with the

17

creation of a San Francisco-Oakland Bay Bridge Division in the Department of Public Works, Purcell was by all means the most logical choice for its engineer. He probably knew before starting, but if not, he very soon found out, that not all of his problems were going to be engineering ones. The original plan had been to float $77,600,000 of bonds to finance the construction but the collapse of the bond market, due to the depression, interfered with this to such an extent that work had to be delayed for a couple of years. By taking advantage of Federal plans to relieve unemployment, a sufficient number of the bonds were sold to the Federal Reconstruction Finance Corporation to permit resumption of the work and, on July 9, 1933, ground was broken by former President Herbert Hoover and President Franklin D. Roosevelt. The bridge was under way.

Purcell took up his work with a full appreciation of the problems that it involved. He expected to encounter some difficulties and in this respect he certainly has had no occasion to be disappointed. Just as in the case of the Golden Gate Bridge, most of the troubles centered around the question of foundations, although the different underwater conditions brought a correspondingly different variety of problems. In the West Bay it was necessary to face the question of putting piers down 100 to 241 feet below the low-water level to a solid footing in bedrock, while a six-mile-an-hour tide, with a rise and fall of about six feet, flowed regularly through a channel as much as 107 feet deep. In the East Bay the water was

18

only fifty feet deep but there was no rock at any practicable depth. Here the question resolved itself into one of sinking pier caissons through this water and the variegated layers of mud, silt, sand and clay, down to a sufficiently solid footing in firm clay as much as 242 feet below the water surface.

It was quite evident that before these piers were ready for the steel superstructure, somebody was going to obtain extensive first-hand experience in what Theodore Roosevelt used to call "the strenuous life." To begin with, the deepest under-water foundations previously built had been only something like 176 feet and these were much smaller piers. Relatively speaking, they were almost tiny beside the tremendous Bay Bridge caissons. Then, there was the matter of that six-mile-an-hour tide pushing its mighty force against the great areas of the large steel-box caissons that would be needed. Finally, there was the question of excavation, for the practical limit of depth for compressed-air caisson workers is generally accepted as about 125 feet! This, of course, put conventional methods entirely out of the picture for several of the fifty-one piers.

The Multiple-dome Caissons.

Out of this welter of difficulties there came the "multiple-dome," a type of pier-sinking box or caisson totally different from anything ever used before. This most original device was a product mainly of the fertile brain of Daniel E. Moran, the "grand old man" of deep-water foundations and one of the Bay Bridge consultants. It combines the advantages of dredging methods with those of the false-bottom-box caisson, in which compressed air is used to keep water and mud out of the under portion so that diggers can work right on the exposed bed of a river. The new Moran caisson, as modified by Purcell's engineers, is a group of fifteen-foot-in-diameter cylinders set vertically and surrounded by a double-wall box of heavy timbers. The cylinders serve as wells for excavating and individual wells could be closed by domed tops to entrap air and thus provide both stability and control during the process of sinking the whole through the mud to a solid footing. The largest caisson, that for the central anchorage, had fifty-five of these cylindrical wells. By pumping air into individual wells (to displace some of the water and thus increase buoyancy), the rate of sinking could be still further controlled to prevent overturning when passing through material of uneven density.

Through the remaining and still-open wells, steel buckets formed like giant clamshells were to be dropped by wire ropes to the bottom and the mud, silt and sand excavated without the necessity of removing any of the water. As one after another well was dredged, the big structure (measuring in the case of the anchorage as much as 197 by 92 feet) would sink through the mud and the various underlying strata. Meanwhile, the domes would be moved and air pressures adjusted where necessary to control the rate of sinking. If one side

began to sink faster than the opposite side, and thus
tilt the big box, additional air pressure would be applied
to the wells at its lower side until excavation proceeded
farther at the others. In this manner the whole structure
could be kept under control during the progress of excavation and sinking. Once it had been worked down to
its final resting place upon the bedrock, the bottom surface was to be examined by a diver, a bed or seal of
concrete would be spread upon the area while still under
water and the wells then filled up with concrete to a
height of about thirty feet, to form the pier base. The
upper portion of each well was to be left filled with
water. During this sinking process, concrete was to be
placed between the double walls of heavy timber to add
weight for sinking and to form the outer shell of the
permanent structure.

This was about the way the whole process was rea-
soned out on paper before the work began. In actual
practice, a variety of unexpected troubles showed up,
to keep engineers and contractors guessing from time to
time. Finally, these "bugs" were eliminated and the four
West Channel piers were sunk to their rocky bases by
use of the new caissons.

In the East Bay, where some of the foundations had
to be carried even deeper, still another variety of caisson
(designed by the Bridge Department in San Francisco)
was used for the three deepest piers. This consisted of a
double-walled steel box which was divided into square
wells by means of partitions running vertically.

21

Through these wells the bottom material was dredged out and the caisson was worked down to a bed in solid clayey sand, one as much as 242 feet below the water level. Domes were not used on these caissons, the lesser depth of water making them unnecessary. Actual construction began in 1933.

The West Channel pier contract was awarded to Transbay Construction Company and the East Channel job to Bridge Builders, Inc. Each firm represented a grouping of four companies bidding jointly, because of the great size of the project and the extent of unknown elements that both undertakings involved. The two contracts, covering only the underwater foundations, represented an estimated price of eleven and a half million dollars—or more than the total cost of many of our largest bridges. The size of this job may be better understood by considering the fact that it included no less than forty-four underwater foundations and seven more on dry land, whereas the usual large bridge job requires only from two to six underwater foundations. To facilitate the work, the Pacific Gas and Electric Company, at a cost of about $60,000, laid a 12,000-volt cable across the bed of the bay with taps running to each of the pier sites. It was estimated that the construction equipment would consume about 11,000,000 kilowatt hours of electric power while the piers were being built. This vast amount of power is enough to supply the average small home for about ten thousand years!

Sinking the Caissons.

To quote Purcell's own words, the sinking of these East and West channel caissons produced "a parade of engineering problems." Some of the practical requirements were contradictory in their nature. On one hand, it was necessary to keep the center of gravity of each caisson low enough to prevent its tipping over, since they were structures extending as much as 107 feet under water even before sinking into the mud. On the other hand, their walls had to be built high enough above the water to ensure against waves breaking over the top and interfering with progress. Down below, the bottom edges had to pass through varied strata that proved to be most uneven in distribution and extremely varied in its supporting ability. Some of it was simply soft mud with no bearing value whatsoever. Other layers were of good hard clay mixed with sand and would have been capable of supporting the completed pier had they not been underlaid, in turn, by softer strata farther down. Each caisson had to be worked through these layers somehow without its overturning suddenly if it encountered mud at one end.

The west tower pier caisson, designated by the engineers as "W-6," gave them many anxious hours at more than one stage of the sinking procedure. On January 14, 1934, dredging was proceeding steadily within the wells of this caisson when the west side began to sink much more rapidly than the east, tilting the whole structure westward. The cutting edge, already about 129 feet under water, had evidently reached one of those soft spots that were to give the engineers plenty to think about before the piers had been finally set down upon the solid bed rock. To correct the tilt, dredging operations were transferred to the other side. After some progress had been made, the big box, with a sudden change of mind, tipped eastward, the top moving about *sixteen feet* in that direction so quickly that the caisson threatened to overturn completely and was saved only by the protective fender.

Considering possible results, that would scarcely have been an appropriate time for some humorist to remark that, at least, their efforts to move it eastward had succeeded.

Fortunately, just such a contingency had been provided for, even if the engineers had not expected quite so much all at once. The heavy timber protective fender and the elaborate anchorage system held the frame of the box against further movement, allowing the workers time to start righting it again. Once more excavation operations were moved to the other side. Into the murky depths of the wells the big clamshell buckets were sent to dig out the mud under the high side. Each bucket bit into the soft material with its great steel jaws and started upwards under the urge of the heavy steel rope by which it was lowered and raised.

Now came a new kind of trouble, directly chargeable to the extreme tilt. The progress of each bucket was

24

short and not exactly calculated to improve the tempers of the already harassed workers, for the excessive tilt caused the buckets to drag against the well sides and each rising bucket was soon snagged against one or other of the numerous cross braces that served to reinforce the interior. No practical amount of muck could be lifted out with the buckets. Various schemes were improvised to guide them clear of the braces, but without success. If the crew had to depend upon their clamshell buckets to finish the job it was evident that the dangerously leaning caisson would never be worked down to its intended low level. Something else would have to be tried.

Water Jets to the Rescue.

So, the very element which was at the root of all of their difficulties was called upon to get them out of this new trouble. Jets of water were introduced into the wells on the high side and the supporting soil was undermined by using this water to flush the material out of place. This expedient was successful and by February 12, 1934, the tilt had been reduced to three feet. By the 15th it again became possible to resume dredging. Nine days later, more trouble of the same kind ensued when the north end of this same caisson suddenly sank into another soft spot, tilting the structure five feet to that side. But, with the understanding gained from previous experience, this was soon rectified and the work continued. By June of 1934, the cutting edge had been worked down to its bed in solid rock 183 feet below the

25

surface of the water, concreting of the base was started and some of the engineers began to catch up on their lost sleep.

Somewhat similar troubles were encountered with certain of the other caissons and one or two produced their own original brand of trouble. In some cases, excavation in the wells had proceeded well on its course when the soft mud decided to ooze back into the holes, working its way under the bottom edge of the caisson as fast as it could be removed and, incidentally, tilting the whole box to that side by undermining its support. In other cases, the sinking progressed fairly well until mud rose far up into some of the domed wells and so effectively plugged their bottom ends that the compressed air was prevented from supporting their side of the caisson. The work of righting another caisson so disturbed the adjacent bed of the bay that piles supporting the working platforms were pushed bodily upwards about five feet, raising the derricks and construction equipment with them.

The big 197- by 92-foot anchorage caisson (the largest caisson ever constructed) had to be set into sloping rock that was twenty feet lower under one side. This is a condition always dreaded in caisson sinking for it has a most uncanny knack of making trouble. Some way had to be found of breaking up and removing enough rock to prepare a reasonably level surface upon which a concrete footing could be laid. A surprisingly simple and thoroughly practical method was found in breaking up

26

the rock by merely dropping a huge five-ton chisel upon it. Loosened and broken material was then removed with the clamshell buckets. This method worked quite satisfactorily until, in one case, a seemingly endless amount of rock was being lifted by the big bucket. A diver sent down to investigate reported that broken rock from the outside was coming into the wells as fast as it was being removed. Excavation at this point was temporarily suspended until cement could be sent down through pipes into the loose rock outside to hold it in place.

Generally speaking, the East Bay foundations gave less trouble than those of the West Bay, the lesser depth of water (50 as against 107 feet) being mainly responsible. The work was not entirely without its interesting diversions, apart from the antics of the caissons. While dredging for pier E-5, one of the buckets brought up something that appeared to be a stone about six or eight inches in diameter. Closer examination having raised some doubts, it was submitted to paleontologists of the University of California who identified it as the tooth of a mammoth that must have roamed the area about 25,000 years ago. Purcell with dry humor remarked that San Francisco Bay must have had its commuters at an earlier date than he formerly realized!

Taking it by and large, the Bay Bridge project never suffered any dearth of gratuitous advice during the construction of those piers. While Purcell's aids and the loyal workers of Transbay Construction Company and Bridge Builders, Inc., were struggling with their gigan-

27

tic caissons, they were carrying on their fight under the eyes of crews and passengers of the great cross-bay ferries that plowed their way regularly across the waters, tracing a course between and around the pier sites. In morning hours the boats would be loaded with commuters on their way to San Francisco offices and shops; in the evening they would pass again as they made their way home after their day's work. Passengers watched the progress with hopeful eyes, for in those great steel boxes dotting the bay lay their prospect of a faster and more convenient daily trip to and from work.

The boat crews were less enthusiastic. Their respect for the men fighting the bay was dampened by the sure knowledge that completion of the bridge meant the end of their ferries. Some of the older, more weatherbeaten, of the ferry crews—men who had spent their lives on the waters of the Bay—shook their heads as the West Bay caissons tilted dangerously. They had their own opinion of men who try to bridge five miles of bay where the water runs as deep as 107 feet. And none too complimentary it was at times. " I told you so," they would confide to the listening ear of some friend on that eventful day in January of 1934, when the "W-6" tilted over until the wake of the passing ferryboat slapped the waters of the bay against its lowered side. These old bay sailors had something at stake and well they knew it. The big bridge was to supplant their cross-bay ferry service that half a century of growth had built into one

of the busiest in the world. "No diver can
a depth," they would confide over a frie
beer at the end of a day's work, when they
one of the East Bay caissons had to go down
And they'd shake a knowing head when son
brought up the question of that funny-looking
tion with all the domes that "this fellow Purce
struggling with out in the bay within the wash
propellers on their trips across.

But, the self-appointed "experts" were wrong.
cell and his contractors did finish the piers, althoug
took some of the most original methods ever used
deep-water excavation. With the piers completed, th
chief worries were over; for, as any of their builders will
tell you, "big bridges are built under water."

Chapter II

Bridges to Roman Aqueducts

Two great San Francisco bridges represent only the latest chapter—the current installment, as it were in an endless serial. It is a story that has been running down through the ages; a story of man's conquest of rivers, bays and canyons, as well as of his mastery over the elements; of his constant struggle for greater and still greater spans and of efforts not always crowned with the complete success of modern attainment. For, in earlier days, bridge failures and bridge accidents were only too frequent. Not until the advent of modern engineering did the building of great bridges become thoroughly scientific and the bridges themselves correspondingly safe.

Bridges came only with civilization and as we trace their development we find ourselves tracing the history of civilization. Primitive man took but little interest in building bridges and he had no desire to build permanent ones. They made it rather too easy for his natural enemies to follow in his trail and the safety of isolation offered by water was eliminated by the bridge. In this association of a feeling of protection with the thought of a body of water we may, perhaps, look for the origin

30

of an old superstition, the once-common belief that no demon, ghost or supernatural body would cross running water. Since primitive man looked upon water as affording protection, what could be more natural than belief that such protection extended to exclusion of supernatural terrors conjured up from his own imagination?

Bridges Follow Civilization.

Since early civilization had made its appearance before permanent bridges were built, we find little evidence of bridge building by primitive peoples. In its earliest stages we begin to see the development of bridges as we follow through the work of early civilizations like those of the Babylonians, Egyptians, Greeks and Romans. First, we find that bridges figured largely in early warfare and it was the military value of bridges in facilitating troop movements that made the Romans the greatest of all bridge builders in early history. Through those Dark Ages that followed the collapse of the great Roman Empire, we find bridge construction virtually abandoned. Its full revival came only with the Napoleonic Wars, and again we note its connection with military strategy.

From this we pass to the more recent stage of railroad building, where the more peaceful pursuits of trade and commerce began to serve as the major incentive to bridge building. Finally we come to the day of the automobile, with a demand for good roads giving tremendous impetus to bridge building. First to the railroad and

31

then to the automobile we owe those economic changes which gave us gigantic structures like the history-making Forth and Brooklyn bridges, as well as the more recent George Washington, Sydney Harbour, Golden Gate and San Francisco Bay bridges. Because of the ambitions of conquest and military strategy arose most of the earlier bridges; because of the peaceful demands of commerce have arisen the greatest of all bridges! This is a logical outcome, perhaps, since modern warfare has become the Great Destroyer that carries down victors with vanquished.

As we trace through the history of every age we find its bridges indelibly marked with the civilization of that period. First we have the simple logs, stone flags and crude little arches contrived in those ages in which civilization itself was yet an experiment. Then we find the stanchness of the old Romans built into their bridges and aqueducts, some of which have been in service for nearly 2,000 years but are still usable to this day. The lapse that we call the "Dark Ages" was reflected in almost complete absence of bridge construction. Then we find the culture of the Renaissance period frozen in marble in some later bridges. Now we see the utilitarianism of the railroad expressed in the sturdy arches of the Stephensons, father and son. In the tracery of wires carrying Roebling's Brooklyn Bridge and in the latticework of Fowler and Baker's majestic Forth Bridge, we find reflections of the Age of Steel. Finally we come to the present with its inconceivably massive Hell Gate

Fig. 6.—This primitive cantilever, constructed entirely of bamboo, spans the Serajoe River in Java.

Fig. 7.—Pontoon bridge over the Rhine at Coblenz.

Fig. 8.—The stately Pont du Gard, an example of Roman engineering.

Arch, the enormous 160-foot width of the Sydney Harbour Bridge and the record-breaking 3,500-foot span of the George Washington Bridge, each representing the spirit of modern engineering expressed in steel. Tomorrow is already almost here, now that we have the still-longer Golden Gate Bridge and the whole series of great structures that form the San Francisco-Oakland Bay Crossing. Bridges and civilization have become synonymous.

Primitive Engineers in Bridge Building.

But we must retrace our steps over this hurried outline if we are to see more of the detail of bridge building through the ages, for bridge design is about the oldest branch of engineering and the building of bridges began even before man had learned how to design the most primitive of them. Those earliest spans were merely logs or tree trunks thrown across streams and the semisavages who built them judged their strength solely by their stiffness. If a bridge did not bend too much they assumed its safety; if it seemed too flimsy, they added another log here and there.

Nobody knows just how many thousands of years ago the first bridge was built and nobody knows just where some early savage thought out the idea of throwing a log over a stream. Most probably a tree blown down by the wind happened to fall across a stream and thus suggested the bridge idea accidentally. In any case, it seems, bridge building began when some prehistoric races

33

started it by throwing trees across streams. These made a poor foothold, so they next arrived at the plan of laying several logs together, making a wider and less precarious path. Emboldened by this success, they tried to bridge wider streams by using crude piers of rough stones for their midstream supports. If the banks of the stream were high, they sometimes built a crude suspension bridge of woven vines, fastening the ends to trees at each side. Semi-savage tribes still build bridges like these and a few of them show that their builders had a vague idea of some of the principles of structural engineering.

With the growth of civilization, some bridges became meeting places of travelers and convenient points at which to break a journey. Settlements on the river banks grew into villages, then into towns, and some of the large cities of the present owe their origin to the construction of a primitive bridge that once carried a well-used trail across a river but which has long since given place to a succession of later bridges.

The beginning of bridge building as a branch of engineering is lost in antiquity. Bridges began, as most other engineering began, with the cut-and-try process which others, less kind than frank, have rather bluntly called the " try and fail " method. The pioneers who used this empirical method made some guesses as to strength required and built accordingly. If the structure collapsed or shook dangerously, they made the next one a little heavier.

Of course this seems crude to us now, since engineers have devised methods of accurately determining all stresses in their structures. But we can easily understand how the ancient builders had no alternative to making a blind try. As they gained experience through successive efforts, some became quite proficient in the art of determining what materials and what forms and proportions were essential to strength. Working only with stone or timber and on a relatively small scale, the early builders could do fairly well even though they had to depend solely upon their judgment. And with one after another of their structures standing for others to copy, even those less competent could follow in their lead. If a small structure carried its loads for a reasonable length of time, the builders felt safe in constructing a larger one with the same proportions.

Eventually they reached the limit of span that could be constructed with the materials and methods available. Hence, it was not until the advent of structural engineering and materials like steel and reinforced concrete that really long-span bridges became possible. Thus for larger bridges mankind had to await the development of modern materials and methods of design.

Although we have little record of their work, the Sumerians, Babylonians, Persians and Chinese were probably the earliest of all bridge builders. In his book *The Sumerians* Leonard Woolley shows a photograph of a brick-arched doorway and vault which were constructed between 3000 and 4000 B.C. by the inhabitants of Sumer, a small country situated on the Persian Gulf and forming part of the area that we now call Arabia. Sumerian ruins unearthed in recent years brought to light the fact that this early people attained what was for that period a high degree of civilization and culture, their work comparing favorably with that of many centuries later and even exceeding it. Although Woolley comments upon their common use of the arch principle in these buildings, no mention is made of bridges constructed by them. However, their use of the arch in buildings suggests the possibility of their having employed it for bridges also.

Relic of another early civilization, we find the ancient Caravan Bridge at Smyrna, Asia Minor, which must be something like 3,000 years old and is believed to be the oldest bridge that is still in use. Among early bridge builders were the Egyptians, whose work usually took the form of stone slabs or brick arches. An arch consisting merely of sloping stones which meet above the opening may be seen at the entrance to the Great Pyramid of Giza. True arches of brickwork have been found in some Egyptian ruins and some of the early Greeks built bridges of stone slabs laid flat upon stone piers. There is good reason to believe that one of the emperors of Babylon constructed a bridge over the Euphrates several hundred years before the birth of Christ; and there is evidence to indicate that the ruins of this bridge may still remain to this day, buried beneath 200 feet of sand with which the winds of centuries entombed a conquered, pillaged and deserted city.

The Chinese, too, were early builders of bridges. Chinese bridges, usually raised over small streams, had sufficient height to permit the passage of small boats. They thus required steep grades or steps leading up to the top, the characteristic form of old Chinese bridges such as are illustrated on the "Willow pattern" teasets of our grandmothers' day. All of these early races undoubtedly built wooden bridges of some type but because of the lesser permanence of the material there are no traces left to late posterity. On the other hand, the greater permanence of stone and its general use by the Romans explains why so many examples of their construction remain to this date.

The Roman Bridges.

The first great era in bridge-building history may be considered as extending over that period covered by the Roman conquest of Europe. Military policy demanded every facility for rapid movement of troops and made the Romans great builders of bridges, just as it made them great builders of roads. The Roman bridges were usually arches built of stone blocks, although some of the earlier examples were of wood. In most cases they spanned rivers over which communication had to be maintained and certain of these bridges figured prominently in Roman history. Most readers will remember the legend immortalized by Lord Macaulay, who put into verse the story of Horatius and his two comrades holding a bridge over the Tiber against the attacking Etruscan army under Lars Porsena. This was in 598

B.C. The bridge was the Pons Sublicius which, unlike later Roman bridges, was constructed of wood.

Despite the military glory attached to her river crossings, the outstanding bridge work of early Rome was her aqueduct construction. Some of these remarkable aqueducts are still in service, although the great majority of them have fallen into ruin or were destroyed by invading hordes during the middle centuries. One of the very earliest of these structures, was started about 312 B.C. This is the Appian Aqueduct, which was constructed under the direction of the builder of the Appian Way, Appius Claudius, for the purpose of bearing into Rome water from springs ten miles away. Of this aqueduct, however, a section of only about 300 feet was carried on arches and most of the construction was underground. During her growth to world dominance, several other important aqueducts were constructed to supply Rome and at one time no less than nine served the ancient city. Some of the later aqueducts, maintained in service to this day, form a part of the water system of the modern city, despite an age of nearly 2,000 years!

As they carried their conquests abroad, the Romans constructed bridges and aqueducts in many parts of Europe where dwellers and visitors can still use the remains of these interesting and often really beautiful structures. Then, of course, we must include mention of Julius Caesar's 1,800-foot, pile supported, wooden bridge over the Rhine, built about 55 B.C., a structure which figures largely in his history of the Gallic War. What this bridge may have lacked in permanence, as compared with stone bridges of the period, it made up in military importance and in the fact that it is reported to have been built in the amazingly short time of ten days.

Caligula's Bridge of Ships.

Not all of the Roman bridges were inspired by military value or utilitarian needs. Personal pomp also served to furnish a motive. To show his power and demonstrate his ability to walk upon the sea, as ordinary mortals walk upon land, Caius Caesar Caligula, early in the Christian era, constructed a bridge of ships across the Bays of Baia and Puteoli, about ninety miles from Rome. The ships were placed in two rows somewhat in crescent arrangement and planking was laid across to connect them, making a bridge about three and a half miles long. It thus completely dwarfed the mile-long floating bridges constructed across the Hellespont by Xeres I, of Persia, in his gigantic campaign against the Greeks more than 500 years earlier. Not only that, but it actually held the record as the longest bridge of any kind ever built until the Southern Pacific Company completed its twenty-mile trestle across the Great Salt Lake in 1903. The ancient pontoon structure continued to hold the record of being the longest *highway* bridge ever built until the four-and-three-quarter-mile bridge over Lake Pontchartrain was completed in 1927, almost nineteen centuries later!

Over the surface of his bridge Caligula ordered earth spread, to make it look like firm ground, and a reminder of the streets of Rome, while upon some of the ships were constructed houses for the reception of the Emperor and his hosts of followers. Fresh water is reported to have been carried to these houses "by pipes" running out from the shore.

When the work was completed, Caligula, in robes lavishly adorned with gold and pearls, rode majestically on horseback across the bridge. Then, to impress all with his power of life and death, he ordered his troops to throw into the sea great multitudes of the spectators, while he and his court watched their drowning struggles as they sank in the waters. Thus the longest bridge of ancient times was built by a mentally deranged emperor solely to gratify his personal pride. But his effort was fruitless, for any glory that might have been carried down in history for him as builder of the bridge has been completely eclipsed by the record of his barbarity. Perhaps it is worth while to add that, some time later, Caligula came to a rather appropriate end at the hands of assassins.

Pont-du-Gard Aqueduct.

During the Roman occupation of the area that is now France, the conquerors built the stately Pont-du-Gard to supply the ancient city of Nîmes with water. Most of this aqueduct is still standing, despite the numerous and destructive wars that have raged over all of Western Europe since that date. It is believed to have been partly destroyed during some wars of the fifth century and subsequently repaired. This structure has a total length of about 885 feet along the top and extends about 160 feet above the water level, its height about equalling that of a fourteen-story building. It consists of three rows of arches superimposed one upon another, following the custom of Roman builders when carrying their structures to great heights. The largest arch, crossing the river below, is slightly over eighty feet in span and was a remarkable piece of engineering for its day. Carried by the top series of arches is the water duct, about four feet wide and slightly more in depth. About 1743, the entire structure was repaired and the lower series of arches sufficiently widened to provide a roadway at one side.

Segovia and Tarragona Aqueducts.

The two aqueducts of Segovia and Tarragona in Spain followed much the same type of construction as that used in the Roman examples just described, differing from those mainly in proportions and the number of arches and in the fact that they consisted of only two-story construction. This difference is quite logical to expect in view of their lesser height of about a hundred feet. Many of the old Roman aqueducts were constructed without the use of cement, excepting where this was necessary to render the duct on top properly water-tight. Stones were cut very carefully, squared to rest firmly one upon another, and in some cases iron bands were used to fasten them in place. In some of the later of the Roman aqueducts, cement masonry construction was adopted. Certain Roman bridges and aqueducts had the stones forming their arches as carefully fitted as if they had been ground together by their builders. The amazing permanence of some of these structures is un-doubtedly accounted for in this way, for there was no cement to disintegrate or be washed away by centuries of exposure to weather.

Looking back nearly 2,000 years in the light of our modern knowledge of bridge construction, it is quite sur-prising to note how little one finds to criticize in the work of the ancient Roman builders. Apparently with-out any method by which they might calculate loads upon component parts of their structures, they showed excellent judgment of the necessary proportions. Un-doubtedly this came from extensive experience and, in-deed, about the only point of serious fault in their work was the great amount of space which they devoted to piers for most of their bridges. These were frequently so heavily constructed as to become serious obstructions and in times of flood the piers impeded the flow of water. Yet despite this and numerous great floods, the bridges usually remained standing until destroyed as the Roman conquerors were driven out when the Em-pire began to lose its hold.

For a perfect illustration of the permanence of the great Roman bridges we have only to look at the Ponte Rotto, which was built over the Tiber about 178 B.C., and has served its purpose for more than 2,100 years! While some of its arches were carried away by one of that stream's great floods, the rest remain and are actually in use to this day! The gap where its missing arches once stood is now bridged by a suspension span, standing in strange contrast to the remaining parts of the original bridge.

Chapter III

From the Dark Ages to the Railroads

FOR several centuries after the fall of Rome bridge building made little progress. Nor was the gap confined to bridges; for history presents the period as an almost complete blank that carried through from about A.D. 500, to something like A.D. 1100, devoid of any constructive human accomplishment. It left several empty pages that we have, by universal consent, labeled the "Dark Ages." Even many of the bridges inherited from earlier ages were allowed to fall into ruin for lack of care. Through these centuries, people continued to travel, although the lack of proper roads and bridges restricted their overland movements within limited areas. Ruling power was too localized to permit development of any comprehensive roadway plans such as those resulting from military needs of the Roman conquerors.

The twelfth century marked a first step towards resumption of bridge building. At that time help came from an unexpected source. Previous accomplishments had been the work of military forces; this new aid came from a totally different quarter, the religious order known as the "Benedictine Monks." Observing the need for bridges at many points, they created a new order under the name of "The Brothers of the Bridge." To this body was assigned the work of creating and maintaining bridges at important crossings. The order collected funds for bridge construction and is credited with erection of bridges at numerous points in Europe.

Historic London Bridges.

Peter of Colechurch, builder of one of the early London bridges, is generally believed to have been a member of the Brothers of the Bridge. History, on this point, is not very specific. We do know, however, that Colechurch began the construction of London's first stone bridge in the year 1176. The bridge took thirty-three years to build and was not opened until 1209. Peter of Colechurch having died in the meantime, his body was interred in a vault above the center pier according to the custom of the order.

The stone bridge replaced an earlier wooden one and its long-drawn-out construction became intertwined with legend which is perpetuated to this day in the old nursery rhyme: *London Bridge Is Falling Down.* For several hundred years this faithful old stone bridge withstood the ravages of time, tide and weather. Although repaired and widened in the meantime, it was not until as late as 1825 that construction of a new bridge was begun.

Like many another of its period, the old bridge was lined with shops. In addition, it carried some apartment houses above and on each side of the roadway, the rents of the shops and buildings being an important source of revenue to the owners. Under three of its arches were machines operated by the ebb and flow of tides to raise water for supplying parts of the old city; at the south end of the bridge there was a gate which had been one of the four main gates to the city since before the Norman Conquest.

This London Bridge, like many of its day, was built and operated under a Government concession. Like many other concessions of that day, the grant was largely influenced by political considerations, an age-old custom which has not yet been fully eradicated from civic life in various parts of the world.

Although the bridge was of stone, the houses and shops evidently were not and to the inflammable nature of their construction were due disastrous fires on more than one occasion. Since it was an important necessity to the city, as well as a good source of revenue to its operators, the bridge was rebuilt after each fire but for many generations the same combustible superstructure was used.

In the year 1212, an outbreak of fire in the buildings at one end of this bridge attracted a great crowd of sightseers. A few thousand persons crowded their way on to the bridge and were too busy watching the blaze to observe in time that a second fire had broken out in another building, behind their backs. Trapped between the two fires and the river, many chose the latter in their desperation. Others tried to save themselves by climbing on board some of the numerous small boats that were attracted to the scene, but the added weight sank many of the boats and those who were in them were drowned. The loss of life was tremendous. Stories handed down from generation to generation usually become exaggerated in the process, and we are told that nearly 3,000 persons lost their lives either by the fire or by drowning. Even after the figure is discounted as having grown in the telling, it remains large enough to rank this old London Bridge fire as the greatest bridge disaster of history. Yet, despite this experience, the houses were rebuilt and other fires occurred in later years.

At another date, some of the houses collapsed into the river, presumably with further loss of life. It was not until the comparatively recent date of 1756 that the bridge houses were finally removed and the entire space devoted to bridge use.

The present London Bridge was begun in 1825 and completed in 1831, being opened on August 1 of that year by King William IV. As traffic grew, some addition became necessary and in 1902 to 1904 the width was increased by twelve feet through rearrangement of the roadway and sidewalks and by means of supporting the new sidewalk upon brackets at each side of the bridge.

Another old stone bridge has been immortalized in verse by the Scottish poet Robert Burns. This is the " Auld Brig o' Ayr," or old bridge of Ayr, built in the thirteenth century, one of the early stone bridges of

47

Scotland. This old structure is still standing, with its four stone arches, each with a fifty-three-foot span, carrying a twelve-foot roadway which is still usable. Because of the interest attached to its antiquity, the bridge is being maintained, although so inadequate that a wider one was constructed nearby.

Some Italian Bridges.

The Ponte Vecchio at Florence, originally built in the twelfth century, is another old stone bridge which stands to this day, although it has undoubtedly been reconstructed since it was first opened. This is one of the few early bridges which still retain the interesting feature of being lined with small shops. The Bridge of Sighs and the Rialto, both of which are in Venice, are two other well-known bridges of the middle centuries which are still in use. The design of the Rialto is often credited to Michelangelo, although this report is disputed by some as inaccurate. Regardless of the truth of the statement, all agree upon the unusual beauty of the bridge with its roofed-over arcade lined with two rows of shops. The roadway runs through the center between the shops, while at each side of it is a footwalk. Two of the striking features of this old bridge are the free use that was made of marble in its construction and the elaborate ornamentation of its structure.

Houses on Bridges.

The custom of building houses on bridges did not confine itself to London but, at one time in the early history

48

FIG. 9.—Paglia Bridge and the famous "Bridge of Sighs" in Venice.

FIG. 10.—This seven-arch bridge carries the famous Chenonceaux Castle in France.

FIG. 11.—The "Auld Brig O'Ayr" mentioned in Burns's verses.

FIG. 12.—Bridge houses 400 years old can be seen at Bad Kreuznach, German resort.

FIG. 13.—Hangman's Bridge is the weird name of this old structure at Nuremberg, Germany.

Fig. 14.—Baltimore's Carroll Viaduct, completed in 1829, is the world's oldest-and-still-used railroad bridge.

Fig. 15.—Old Chain Bridge over the Lehigh, built in 1826 and removed in 1933.

of bridge building, was quite prevalent elsewhere. Although, as we have noted, the old London Bridge was long since removed to make way for the present structure, in many parts of Europe some bridges of this kind are still standing. One of the oldest of these quaint structures is the Nahe River Bridge in Bad Kreuznach, a picturesque German health resort. This old bridge is believed to have been constructed more than 400 years ago and the apartment buildings which are carried on its mid-river piers are still occupied. Towering three stories and an attic above the roadway, the little houses are partly supported with wooden braces fashioned much like stilts. With their quaint peaked roofs and their tiny windows, these houses might well have been the inspiration for illustrations in some old book of nursery rhymes.

Another old bridge of equal interest and about equal antiquity stands in the city of Nuremberg, sometimes known as the "City of Toys" because so many are made there. This is the Henkersteg, crossing the Pegnitz River in the older part of the city, its picturesque appearance belying the grewsome name of "Hangman's Bridge" which it has carried down from earlier years.

Not all of the houses built upon bridges were confined to the modest station of the little apartments on the Bad Kreuznach and other bridges. Throughout France, in particular, we find many cases where the more wealthy resorted to similar but much more palatial structures. Chenonceaux Castle in Touraine, extending over a

49

seven-arch bridge, is an excellent example of this kind. The stately and imposing structure of the castle, with its fine architecture, is counted among one of the sights of this district and is pictured frequently in the tourist and railway guides to France.

Entirely apart from its unusual construction, Chenonceaux Castle has an interesting history. It is one of the oldest in Touraine and was given by Henry the Eighth to Diane de Poitiers, who in turn gave it to Catherine de Medicis, the Queen of France who is best remembered as instigator of the massacre of St. Bartholomew. One can easily imagine with what facility enemies were disposed of in a castle part of which was directly over the water.

Napoleonic Conquests Revive Bridge Building.

Despite occasional and interesting bridges such as we have described, it was not until the Napoleonic Wars that a true renaissance of bridge construction really began. With the dawn of a new era of conquest, the military strategists awoke to renewed appreciation of the value of bridges in their campaigns. Fully as well as the conquerors of centuries long past, the little Corsican General realized the military importance of bridges in transportation and communication. Accompanying his campaigns there came a wave of bridge building that represented the first large-scale building since the Roman period. Across Europe swept Napoleon's forces, conquering and building bridges as they went.

50

From the Roman period up to the middle centuries, most bridge arches were comparatively small. One authority gives the average span as something like twenty-five feet, only a few structures showing any that surpassed that size. With increased need for transportation as the years passed, this span was gradually increased until many bridges with seventy-five-foot arches (and a few of greater size) had been built, before the middle of the eighteenth century. Yet, even this figure indicated no gain over some old Roman aqueducts.

With the inception of engineering methods in the mid-eighteenth century, bridge spans began to show substantial increase, but real development came only with the railroads. In the new mode of transportation not only must much heavier loads be provided for, but there was also the necessity of eliminating sharp turns and steep grades, making the need of bridges much more acute. Where wagon roads could wind their ways down mountain sides at steep grades, the railroad often had to be bridged over valleys, and where horse carts could depend upon light ferries or upon fords in shallow parts of rivers, the railroad had to wait for bridges. Mute evidence of what bridges meant to railroads is found in the frequency with which the name of George Stephenson, Chief Engineer of the original Stockton and Darlington Railway, appears in association with bridge building in the early days of railroads. Stephenson and his son Robert, who followed in his father's footsteps, were each responsible for many stone bridges and viaducts for English railroads and for some cast-iron and wrought-iron bridges also.

The Influence of Railroads upon Bridges.

Before the days of railroads, bridges were required to carry only the much smaller loads represented by horse-drawn wagons and pedestrians. Furthermore, there was no great objection to having a very sharp turn at each end of the bridge nor was there serious drawback to having a steep incline of the roadway approaching the bridge from each side. Very frequently the bridge would be required to cross a stream located at the bottom of a valley with high mountains on each side. To save cost and to simplify his problems by making the bridge smaller, the builder would put it across the stream at the bottom of this valley, regardless of the fact that the roads approaching it on either side must be steep and winding.

When the building of bridges for railroads was in question, all of this had to be changed, for the trains could not run up or down steep hills nor could their tracks bend sharply around turns as could common roadways. Often the bridge level must be raised sufficiently to eliminate the grades and sharp turns and sometimes a whole valley must be bridged, instead of merely a small stream at the bottom. As if this, in itself, did not create sufficient of a problem for bridge builders, railroad trains were far heavier than horses and wagons. To make matters even more complicated, the weight to be carried became greater and greater as better and bigger locomotives and cars were developed. Almost immediately, the construction of bridges became a problem of first importance to railroad builders and it has retained that position ever since.

As a result of this situation, bridge building underwent rapid development during the period of railroad building that started in the earlier half of the nineteenth century. From 1830 to 1850, a period of great activity in railroad construction in Great Britain, there was a call for the construction of numerous brick and stone arches with spans bridging as much as 180 feet and heights up to 150 feet. This work probably represents the first substantial advance over the bridge building of the early Romans, although a gap of some eighteen centuries stretched between. Bridges now increased in height, span, strength and numbers with such rapidity that more advance was made in a fifty-year period than had been accomplished in the entire 1,800 years directly preceeding! The age of revival in bridge making witnessed the construction of works like the Menai Straits Suspension Bridge and the Brittania Tubular Bridge in Great Britain and the Morlaix Viaduct in France.

Perhaps the most important advance, however, was not so much in the size of the bridges actually constructed as in the fact that more scientific methods of design were developed. Engineers began to work out methods of analyzing stresses in bridge structures and, for the first time, applying iron and steel to the construction of their designs. Without such developments, the great bridges of today would have remained impossible dreams. Much credit for modern accomplishments in bridge building must be granted to the pressure for stronger and larger bridges that resulted from the building of railroads.

Erectors of many stone bridges "builded better than they knew," as the old saying goes. Such is the inherent strength of this type of construction that many a stone bridge is today carrying loads far beyond the most extravagant expectation of its designers although, perhaps, a century or more has passed since its construction. Many old stone railroad bridges are still in use. Where they have been replaced, the reason is the necessity of additional tracks more often than it is the weaknesses developing after years of use.

One is not accustomed to find many "oldest" things in the United States, yet we do have in this country what is believed to be the oldest railway bridge in existence that is still in use. This is the Carrollton Viaduct of the Baltimore and Ohio Railroad, a bridge which certainly deserves a place in any mention of this kind. Built originally in 1829, it was presumably designed for locomotives of that period—which weighed only about three and a half tons. Indeed, the first locomotive to use it was the historic little "Tom Thumb." Yet today, without any change in its construction, this same bridge is carrying heavy modern trains pulled by locomotives that alone weigh over 350 tons apiece, or *one hundred times* as much as those for which it was intended! Even this does not tell the whole story, for the speed of trains has increased tremendously. When we consider the vibration of heavy, fast-moving modern trains, it becomes evident that the old Carrollton Viaduct is carrying many more than a hundred times the load that its designers expected! Yet this interesting old bridge with its arch of cut stone, spanning a small stream near Baltimore, continues to serve its purpose as well as it did when railroads were new.

The stone arch viaduct across the Patapsco River at Relay, Maryland, built in 1835, is another old bridge on the same railroad and has just rounded out its first century of continuous service, with the prospect of many years yet to come.

An interesting stone bridge, of more recent date, is the Pennsylvania Railroad's great Rockville Bridge with its forty-eight stone arches carrying four tracks of railroad over the Susquehanna River, five and a half miles north of Harrisburg, Pennsylvania. Construction of this bridge required no less than 440,000,000 pounds of stone, according to estimates of the road's engineers. Among later masonry arch bridges in Europe, the Landwasser Viaduct of the Swiss Albula Railway is particularly striking. Not only is its height of 213 feet unusual for a stone bridge, but this structure is built on a curve, in defiance of the traditional practice of building bridges in straight lines. Although the whole structure forms a curve, each of the arches is, in itself, actually straight; but it takes an observing eye to detect this fact. The radius of curvature is surprisingly small for a railroad structure, no more than 328 feet. The Viaduct has six arches, each with an opening of sixty-six feet but of varying height according to the terrain of the gorge below. It terminates abruptly against the face of a cliff through which the railroad proceeds by means of a tunnel.

Modern Stone Bridges.

Because of their adaptability to aesthetic design, as well as their everlasting permanance, stone bridges are still being constructed and those already built are likely to remain with us for many generations to come. Nowadays, however, the tendency is to restrict this type of bridge to monumental structures, park drives and parkways, where appearance is the factor of paramount importance. Most recent practice has been to construct reinforced-concrete-arch or steel-frame bridges and to face them with stone so that to the eye they appear to be stone bridges, although the concrete or steel may actually carry the entire load. This use of steel frames or concrete for the main load-carrying structure possesses the advantage of reducing construction cost, while the stone facing retains the beauty of an all-stone structure.

Since these modifications in construction came into use, some new bridges are not what they seem. Many of the recently built and strikingly beautiful "stone" bridges that grace our modern parkways throughout the United States are really only faced with stone, although they are in every way as permanent as if built of stone throughout. The reinforced-concrete and steel-frame types also have certain other advantages in addition to lower construction cost. One factor of considerable importance is the greater range of arch proportions which these methods of design permit. In this way bridges can be constructed with only a small rise to the arch, a condition which might often prohibit the use of true stone arches. For stone arch construction requires sufficient depth and curvature to provide a "wedging" effect when all of the arch stones are in place. Indeed, if the arch stones are carefully fitted, a well designed stone arch would support itself and carry its load without the necessity of cement to fasten the stones together.

Chapter IV

Wooden Trusses Lead to Iron Trusses

Covered Wooden Bridges.

WE HAVE already referred to the fact that the first material used for bridge construction was wood, since this was the most convenient material for early races to handle. Wooden bridges have been built probably since time immemorial and, although in recent times lumber has been supplanted by other materials to a very great extent, some wooden bridges are constructed to this day. The earliest wooden bridges were of the beam type and of very short span, the spans limited by the practical depth of beams which could be sawn out of rough logs. After this limit had been reached and for places where it was not practicable to construct piers in the stream, builders of wooden bridges began to cast around for some method of spanning wider rivers without the necessity of constructing a more expensive (although more permanent) stone or brick arch. Wooden bridges were built by carpenters accustomed to building houses. It seems only natural, then, that they

58

hea
nect   g   . This
arran   very practi   although somewhat
crude,   l was the method used in the covered
bridg   ame into existence in this country during
the Colon   ys and the early years of the republic.

Many have sked why these bridges were always covered. It seems to be generally agreed that the purpose was to protect the structure from some of the effects of weather. Since it would have been necessary to cover only the trusses themselves, the explanation does not seem entirely adequate. It is likely that the builders may have been influenced also by their experience in constructing frame houses.

At one time there were many bridges of this type in the United States but a large proportion, fallen victims to "progress," have been replaced by others of more modern construction. Of late there has been a growing appreciation of the historical value and interest attached to our old covered bridges and highway officials are now showing a tendency to preserve, instead of replace, them. When they become unsafe or inadequate, a new bridge is built near by and the old one is left intact to be kept as a local point of historic interest. Throughout the state of Pennsylvania, certain of the New England states, and a few others, some old covered wooden bridges can still be seen and they are likely to be preserved for posterity.

wooden ... Ame... the Colonial days. It may, therefore, c... ich of a surprise to them to learn that such ... have been in use in several parts of Europe ai ... bridge which is probably the oldest covered w... bridge in the world is not in the United States but in Switzerland! This is the ancient Kapell Bridge of Lucerne, built in 1333, or more than 600 years ago and nearly 160 years before Christopher Columbus had even discovered America! The Kapell Bridge, which crosses the River Reuss at Lucerne, is believed to have been originally 880 feet long but a fire in 1833 destroyed a portion of one end. Instead of rebuilding all of the burned portion, the restorers filled in the quay, to connect with the remaining part.

This bridge is unusual in many ways other than from the point of view of its great antiquity. To start with, its wandering form, crossing the river diagonally, almost suggests an illustration from one of our Mother Goose Books. The structure is wholly of wood and much of the original material remains, although in certain cases the beams have had to be replaced. Not only is it the oldest, but it is also one of the best preserved, of covered wooden bridges. The structure rests upon piles made of wood except near the midstream tower, where a stony bed made it necessary to use some other kind of foundation and the early builders substituted supports built of stone blocks. The roadway—or perhaps we should say footway, since it is now used only as a foot-bridge—is twelve feet wide and the shingled roof is slightly wider, giving an overhang on each side. Connected with the bridge and located about midstream is a tower which originally formed part of the city's fortifications but is now used as a storehouse for city documents. Piles and beams used in the construction of the Kapell Bridge are of oak, their age testifying eloquently to the unusual permanence of that kind of lumber. Adjacent to the old bridge is one of modern construction which forms a startling contrast with its neighbor.

The First Trusses.

Bridges of the beam type and the simple truss type began as wooden structures and for some time after they were first introduced all trusses were built of wood. One of the oldest of wooden truss bridges is that crossing the River Reuss at Bremgarten, a little town in the Canton of Argovie in Switzerland. Although built between 1544 and 1550, this historic bridge is still in a good state of preservation.

While there are many varieties of truss designs in use, all are based upon the principle of creating a structure formed of triangles. Since the shape of a triangle cannot be altered without shortening or lengthening at least one of its sides, each triangle forms a structure which is as rigid as the properties of the material permit. Thus we can build rigid structures in almost any desired form

61

if we design them in the form of properly connected triangles.

When this principle was first stumbled upon by the early carpenters who built our wooden bridges, they had no method for determining the stresses in each portion of their trusses. While they knew how to build a rigid structure in this manner, they did not know how to estimate its strength and they had to rely upon their judgment which, in this case, meant simply guesswork based upon experience. In the early part of the nineteenth century, engineers developed scientific methods of analyzing and calculating stresses in trusses. Beginning with the simple "king-post" truss, they finally worked up to those elaborate structures which comprise some of our modern bridges.

How a Truss Works.

To use as an example the simplest form of truss, let us consider a bridge of planks resting upon end supports which are so far apart that the planks are not strong enough to support a vehicle without some aid. Suppose we place under the center of this plank bridge some vertical struts or "king-posts" and run cables or rods from end to end of the bridge, passing each of them under the bottom end of the king-post. Then let us fasten the ends of all rods securely, so that a side view of the bridge looks like the first diagram on page 63.

Our plank bridge has now become a truss bridge of the very simplest type. As one can readily see, it will not only be stronger but it will also be much more rigid than it was before we added the trussing below. If this whole arrangement is turned up the other way, the same principle applies except that the stresses become re-

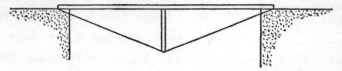

Side view of a simple "king-post" truss.

versed; portions which were formerly in tension are now in compression and those formerly in compression are now in tension. Here we have the basic principle of all trusses, for we can combine these triangular elements to form a great bridge truss consisting of innumerable simple elements connected together. This little diagram shows the evolution of the modern truss from the original king-post:

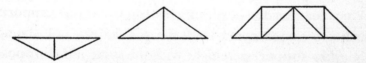

Evolution of the modern truss.

Using this knowledge, early designers of practical trusses began by taking timbers for the members which are subjected to compression and iron rods for those which are subjected to tension. In the period ranging around 1840, scientific methods of truss analysis had their beginning and in 1847 Squire Whipple published his classic treatise on truss design. This work laid the

63

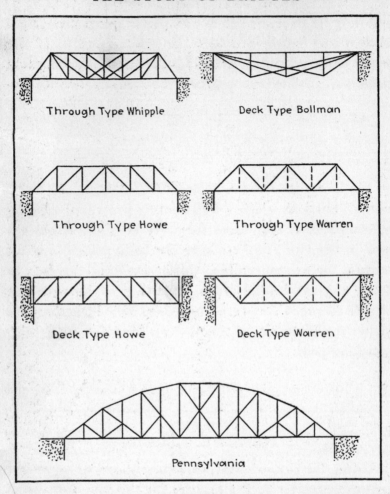

Through Type Whipple

Deck Type Bollman

Through Type Howe

Through Type Warren

Deck Type Howe

Deck Type Warren

Pennsylvania

These diagrams show a few of the many kinds of trusses used for bridges. The lines of the simple "king-post" truss can be recognized in the old Bollman, a type no longer built. Broken lines in some of the diagrams represent parts which are not essential to the truss but which are often added for the purpose of bracing the bridge floor or stiffening some of the compression members. "Through truss" bridges are those in which the roadway passes between the trusses; "deck truss" bridges are those in which the roadway is placed above the trusses.

FIG. 16.—This quaint Swiss wooden bridge at Lucerne is now more than 600 years old. (*Photograph by Franz Schneider.*)

Fig. 17.—This covered wooden bridge has served the town of Bremgarten, Switzerland, since 1550.

Fig. 18.—Brittania Tubular Bridge over Menai Straits, completed in 1850.

Fig. 19.—Victoria Tubular Bridge over the St. Lawrence, opened in 1860, replaced in 1898.

Fig. 20.—Landwasser Viaduct, an interesting bridge on the Swiss Rhaetian Railway. (*Photograph by E. Meerkamper.*)

foundations for modern stress analysis and paved the way for the transition from wood to iron and steel, which followed a few decades later. The Whipple, Howe, Pratt and many other forms of truss design followed one another in rapid succession, each type being named after its inventor. These trusses were used in constructing wooden bridges and while they were antedated by trusses of diagonal latticework, the earlier designs were built before methods of calculating stresses became known. Hence, it is customary to regard the era of trusses as having started with the work of Whipple and his contemporaries rather than with the earlier lattice trusses. Many wooden bridges of the truss type were built in the United States and were greatly favored in the early days of railroads, when they were called upon to carry greater loads over greater spans than was possible for most highway bridges of the same period.

The Period of Wrought-iron Bridges.

About the time that designers were evolving their first ideas of truss design and embodying the results in their structures of wood, there occurred two incidents which were destined to revolutionize bridge construction in subsequent years. One was the use of steel eyebars in a Vienna suspension bridge, built in 1828. This was the first recorded use of steel in any type of bridge and it constituted an experiment which, by reason of its cost, was not repeated for several decades thereafter. For steel was still being "hand made" by the old-fashioned methods and was far too expensive to compete with other bridge-building materials. The second of the two incidents was the construction of a relatively short-span railroad bridge near Glasgow, Scotland, in 1841. This bridge might long since have been forgotten had not its designer taken the radical departure of using rolled-iron beams or girders instead of building it of stone like most other railroad bridges of the time. The innovation was quickly taken up by others and bridges of wrought-iron girders soon came into general use both for railroads and for highways. In comparatively few years thereafter, wrought iron also began to displace wood in the construction of trusses. From the use of timbers and iron tie rods, it was only a small and almost obvious step to build trusses wholly of wrought iron, once the principles of stress analysis had been established. The first iron truss bridge that was constructed for heavy loads was probably one built for the Reading Railroad in 1845; from that period on a more or less steady transition from wood to metal took place in railroad-bridge truss construction.

In their search for a design sufficiently rigid for railroad use, some engineers built tubular bridges of wrought iron. This type never became very popular, although several bridges of the kind were constructed. The most outstanding among these is undoubtedly the old Brittania Bridge over Menai Straits in North Wales, near the equally historic and fully as interesting suspension bridge crossing the same body of water. The

66

Brittania is constructed in the form of two rectangular tubes, built mainly of wrought-iron plates. Each tube is used to carry over the Straits one of the two tracks of the Chester and Holyhead Railway. The bridge was designed by the famous railroad engineer Robert Stephenson and, although completed about 1850, is still in regular use. It consists of two main spans of 460 feet each, two side spans and two approach spans. Some doubt regarding the strength of the bridge under the vibration of locomotives and trains inspired a fear that suspension cables or chains might be necessary. To allow for these, the towers carrying the tubes were extended considerably above the track level for support of a suspension system. After completion of the bridge, its designers were pleasantly surprised to find their work sufficiently rigid without the suspension chains and, hence, they were never added. Despite the greatly increased weight of modern trains, the bridge has continued in use to this day without any suspension chains.

Subsequent to the erection of this Brittania Bridge, other tubular bridges were built both in England and America, the largest being the old Victoria Bridge over the St. Lawrence at Montreal. This was a somewhat similar design, also one of Robert Stephenson's, and was built a few years after the Brittania, being opened in 1860. To meet the needs of increased traffic, it was replaced by a larger bridge of the truss type in 1898. When improved methods of designing truss bridges had become available, the tubular type was soon discarded.

It is perhaps quite natural to find that, as the oldest railroad in America, the Baltimore and Ohio Railroad includes among its excellent modern bridges some of the earliest of the iron-truss type. In some cases the older bridges are still in place, although supplanted in use by others of recent construction. In a few cases some of the venerable bridges—with proper maintenance—still continue to perform their function satisfactorily. Recently at the Harper's Ferry, West Virginia, crossing of the Potomac, we could see three generations of bridges side by side, a unique situation that was terminated only by the disastrous floods of early 1936. Although each of the earlier bridges had, in turn, been supplanted by a later bridge, the earliest one was allowed to remain because of historic interest and the fact that it could still be used for certain purposes.

The first bridge at this point was built in 1836, using stone piers which are still in place. In 1852 a Bollman truss bridge with iron compression members and iron tie rods was substituted for the original wooden truss bridge on these piers. This iron bridge was the first of the Bollman trusses and it remained in place, a veteran of many floods, until the record rise of water in 1936 swept it away. The increased weight of locomotives and trains had made it desirable to construct a heavier bridge; so, in 1894 another span, built in a later design and of structural steel, was erected near the old one. The second, in its turn, became insufficient to cope with the growing weight of traffic and still another bridge was erected in 1931. This time one of steel-plate girder construction was used and again the older bridge was left intact, thus giving Harper's Ferry, from 1931 until 1936, three generations of bridges standing side by side!

Wendell Bollman, for whom this early type of truss was named, was one of four carpenters employed to lay the first lengths of track for the original stretch of line of the Baltimore and Ohio Railroad in Baltimore. It may be necessary to explain that in those days the tracks consisted of wooden rails faced with metal straps—hence the need of carpenters in track construction. Bollman proved to be so ingenious in building bridges that the railroad soon advanced him and eventually he became "master of the road" in charge of the entire right-of-way of the line. Bollman devised the truss, used on many of the old Baltimore and Ohio Railroad bridges, which might be considered a development of the simple king-post truss that we spoke of in describing the principles of trusses. The first Bollman truss bridge at Harper's Ferry, with its 124-foot span, was considered a considerable achievement in its day. As evidenced by the faithful way in which it performed its service for many years, the judgment of that day was fully warranted. For, as we have said, the old bridge remained in place until 1936, even though outmoded by increased weight of trains and not used for railroad traffic after 1894.

Chapter V

An Age of Iron Bridges

ALTHOUGH men had built bridges of wood and stone from time immemorial, it was only in the latter half of the eighteenth century that any substantial use was made of iron in bridge building. The first iron bridges were really of cast iron, a number having been built in which the castings formed segments of the bridge arches somewhat after the manner of stone bridges. At a later date some cast iron was used in girders, ribs and other forms. One of the most interesting of the early cast-iron bridges was that built at Coalbrookdale, to cross the River Severn. This structure was constructed in 1776 and had a span of slightly over one hundred feet. It was supported by a series of segmental cast-iron ribs which were nearly semicircular and it was the first bridge constructed exclusively of cast iron. Between the date of its erection and the close of the nineteenth century many cast-iron bridges were built. However, with the introduction of wrought iron, this more ductile, stronger and more reliable material eventually displaced cast iron just as in turn, some years later, it was to be displaced by the still stronger steel.

Early Suspension Bridges.

From the primitive attempts of prehistoric times, the constructing of suspension bridges (structures carried by ropes, chains or cables) remained at a virtual standstill until the application of wrought iron and steel to bridge building. In the many centuries that intervened but few suspension bridges were constructed. On such as there were, ropes were used and only light traffic was carried. At the beginning of the nineteenth century the need for stronger long-span bridges led their builders to consider the suspension principle, with iron-bar chains substituted for the ropes formerly used. The first bridge embodying the principles of modern suspension-bridge design is generally believed to be the chain bridge constructed over Jacobs Creek in Pennsylvania by James Finley in 1801.

Numerous small chain bridges followed, the one of most outstanding importance among these earlier ones being the 244-foot span constructed in 1810 across the Merrimac River, three miles above Newburyport, Massachusetts. This bridge, constructed according to the designs of Finley, replaced an earlier one of wood. It had two roadways, each fifteen feet wide, carried independently of each other by two sets of triple iron chains. For practical purposes it might almost be considered as two bridges side by side with common towers and piers. The towers of timber were sheathed and shingled somewhat after the manner of frame-house construction and they rested upon masonry abutments

71

at each side of the river. This bridge remained in service until fairly recently, having been reconstructed in 1909.

Thomas Telford, who began work as a stone mason and lived to become one of the greatest engineers of history, in 1826 completed his famous chain bridge with its 580-foot span over the Menai Straits in Wales. This bridge was carried by sixteen main chains arranged in groups of four, each of its two roadways being carried by two groups of chains. About thirteen years after its completion the bridge was seriously damaged by windstorm but was repaired and is still in use. This bridge was built to carry highway and pedestrian traffic. It is located only several hundred feet away from the Brittania Tubular Bridge, which was built later to carry rail traffic and which we have already described. The Menai suspension bridge has towers and side spans of masonry construction, built up from a foundation upon rock. Ties, corresponding in their spacing to the spacing of the main span suspenders, are carried from the side-span masonry up to the suspension chains, presumably for the purpose of relieving the anchorages of all vertical pull. For several years this bridge retained the record of having a longer span than any other structure in the world.

This distinction was lost in 1834 when there was completed at Fribourg, Switzerland, the Pont du Gotteron, a suspension bridge designed by M. Chaley and having a span of 870 feet from the points of cable support. Because of the location of these supports, a short distance back of the edge of the bridge abutments, the span of its floor was somewhat less than that of the cables. The suspension system used for this bridge consisted of four iron-wire cables and represented the first use of iron wire instead of chains for suspension. The cables were strung from the rocks at one side of the chasm to those at the other. Very little masonry was used, the foundations being hewn out of the cliffs and the cable ends being anchored in the rock on each side. The suspension system of this bridge was rather unusual also in that its cables started from a rock high above the bridge at one end and entered the opposite rocks near the bridge floor level. This bridge continued in use until 1924, although it was reinforced in 1881 by the addition of two new suspension cables.

Numerous other suspension bridges were built in the years following the completion of the Gotteron Bridge, but until 1848 its span was not exceeded by that of any other structure. When this record changed hands, it passed to a new structure in the United States. This was the Ohio River Bridge at Wheeling, West Virginia, with a center span of 1,010 feet, designed by Col. Charles Ellet and completed in 1848. About five years later, the Wheeling bridge was seriously damaged by a tornado but was repaired under the direction of John A. Roebling, the bridge engineer who later became identified with the designing and construction of the Brooklyn Bridge.

In 1850 the construction of a suspension bridge designed by Edward W. Serrell was begun at Lewiston, about two miles below Niagara Falls, New York. The towers were spaced 1,040 feet apart and the bridge span was about 850 feet, wind-bracing guy wires being carried from the lower side of the bridge floor back to each side of the gorge to furnish protection against severe storms. In 1861, these wires were temporarily removed and in their absence the bridge was completely destroyed by wind. It was not reconstructed but in 1899, or about thirty-eight years later, a new bridge (designed by L. L. Buck) was erected in its place.

A few years after the completion of the Serrell Bridge at Lewiston, Roebling designed and constructed the first Niagara railroad bridge. In the design stiffening trusses were used for the first time in order to provide sufficient rigidity for railroad use. Roebling's Niagara bridge had a span of 821 feet and two decks, the lower one carrying a fifteen-foot roadway while the upper carried a single railroad track. The first stiffening trusses were of timber and extended between the two decks. In 1880 these were replaced by steel trusses and at various times important repairs were made to keep the bridge in safe condition. By 1897, however, the span, having outlived its usefulness, was replaced by a rigid steel arch bridge.

After several delays, due first to financing difficulties and then to the Civil War, Roebling finally completed in 1867 a 1,057-foot span over the Ohio River at Cincinnati. In this same year construction of a 1,268-foot suspension bridge over the Niagara River began and in 1869 it was completed. This last bridge was designed by Samuel Keefer, iron wire cables carried upon wooden towers were used and, in addition to guy wires, stiffening trusses were provided to protect the bridge from wind damage. Despite these precautions, the bridge was blown down in 1889 but was replaced immediately with a new structure in which were used steel-wire cables carried upon steel towers. Nearly ten years later this bridge, in turn, was replaced by a steel arch. During all of this period suspension-bridge construction was proceeding in other parts of the world also, but the American bridges were so much longer that they continued to monopolize interest so far as this type of structure was concerned. Outstanding European bridges built during these years followed other principles of construction, being generally cantilever or arch bridges.

The Principle of Cantilever Bridges.

The principle of a cantilever bridge is best understood by thinking of each span as consisting of two great brackets, each of which rests upon a pier and is anchored behind that pier. The outer ends of the brackets either meet in the center of the span or they are connected by a simple truss which bridges the gap. So far as we know, the very first bridges embodying cantilever principles were built in certain countries of the Far East. These were constructed of heavy timbers rigidly fastened, in one way or another, at their shore ends while the outer ends projected out over the stream towards the center, where timbers from each side met. Little or no progress was made in the development of cantilever bridges until the advent of iron and steel, materials more adaptable to this form of design than are wood, stone or concrete.

One of the earliest of large bridge structures to incorporate cantilever principles in its design was Gerber's three-span bridge built over the Main at Hassfurt, Germany, in 1867. Hence, in Germany, cantilever bridges are called "Gerber bridges." This was a highway bridge with a central span of 124 feet supported by two piers located in the river, side spans continuing the bridge to each side. About this same period, there were constructed in accordance with the designs of an English engineer, Smedley, many bridges which combined the features of the suspension and the cantilever. Smedley's bridges used a cantilever truss extending out from each pier to give the floor partial support from the under side, while a suspension system carried the rest of the load from above.

Since it depends upon the principle of a bracket, the cantilever is inherently much more rigid than a suspension bridge. Because of this rigidity and their unsatisfactory experiences with early suspension bridges, railroad engineers soon began to consider the use of cantilever bridges. The first of the type constructed for rail use was built at Posen, Poland, in 1876. It had five spans of which the center span was 148 feet long. Almost at the same time, another cantilever railroad bridge was constructed at Dixville, Kentucky, with three spans of 375 feet each. Up to that time all cantilever bridges had been designed so that the two arms met in the center of the span. In 1883 a radical departure was taken in designing of the Michigan Central Railroad's bridge over the Niagara River. This structure comprised cantilever arms which did not meet in the center of the span, but instead supported a center section designed as a simple truss. This type of design is known as the "suspended span cantilever" and has since come into very general use. The Niagara Bridge had two intermediate towers, a span of 495 feet between tower centers and a total length of 850 feet. This structure has since been replaced by an arch bridge of stronger construction to provide for increased loads due to heavier locomotives and trains.

The Tay Bridge Disaster.

The introduction of iron trusses brought its own problems to the designers and builders of bridges and some bridge collapses which occurred during that period were directly due to the designers' inexperience with the material. One of these was the collapse of the Firth of Tay Bridge in Scotland, on the night of December 29, 1879, the worst bridge accident since the advent of modern engineering. For about two years after its completion in 1877, this bridge was ranked as one of the wonders of the world, with its eighty-four truss spans, each 200 feet in length and carried upon piers at a height of about eighty-eight feet above the water. The trusses were built of wrought iron, for the bridge was completed just prior to the advent of steel construction. The supporting piers were constructed upon a base of brick and carried up with stone to a height of several feet above the water level. From there up to the trusses were columns consisting of six cast-iron pipes braced with iron lattices running from pipe to pipe.

After carrying its loads apparently satisfactorily for about two years, the bridge suddenly collapsed, thirteen spans going down without a warning while a trainload of passengers was crossing. Not a soul was saved to give a first-hand report of the disaster. The loss of life was estimated at 80 to 100 or more—the circumstances of the accident leaving some doubt as to the total, since bodies may have been carried out to sea. This collapse caused a tremendous sensation, for the bridge had been designed and constructed under the direction of Sir Thomas Bouch, to that time considered one of the leading bridge builders of the period. Indeed, at the time of the collapse he was actually at work upon plans for a still greater bridge of the suspension type which was to span the Firth of Forth.

With characteristic British thoroughness, a Government investigation was undertaken to determine the cause of the collapse and in its report a few months later the designer was severely censured for his inadequate allowance for wind loads. On the night of the disaster the wind was reported to have attained the terrific velocity of seventy-two to eighty miles an hour and everything indicated that the bridge was simply blown down. The accident resulted in engineers giving much greater attention to wind loads. When Sir John Fowler and Sir Benjamin Baker supplanted Bouch as designers of the new Forth Bridge, they went to such extremes with their precautions that they allowed for wind pressure nearly twice as much as we allow today.

News of the Tay Bridge disaster reached America quickly by means of the Atlantic cables, which were still new enough to be somewhat of a novelty, although the first had been laid nearly a generation earlier. The *Engineering News* in its issue of Saturday, January 3, 1880, made it the subject of an editorial, the very brevity of which only served to emphasize the harrowing features of the tragedy. Explaining that the news had just reached him as the paper was going to press, the Editor referred to thirteen of the eighty-four spans as having "disappeared" during the night. From the yellowed pages of more than half a century ago we read: "A passenger train composed of six coaches, one locomotive and the brakeman's van and carrying an unknown number of passengers was seen to enter the northern end of the bridge and cross into the center or channel spans. A few moments later a shower of fire (it was at night) was seen to fall into the river below. These facts, with the floating debris visible in the morning light are the only ones to tell the fate of the train with its living freight."

79

Such was the effect upon Bouch, the designer, that he died within a few years after the catastrophe. Eventually, a new Tay Bridge was built at the same site but a lesson had been learned and the new bridge was a very much stronger one. Incidentally, this time steel was used in place of wrought iron.

The ill-fated Tay Bridge was one of the last of the great iron bridges, for a new and stronger material was soon to become available. Its history began in 1855 when there occurred an event which, combined with the growing knowledge of truss design, was to make possible the great bridges of today. This event was the invention of the Bessemer process, a new and more economical method of eliminating from pig iron its excess carbon and silicon in preparing it for the manufacture of steel.

Within ten years, Bessemer's invention was in general use, revolutionizing the production of steel and greatly reducing its cost. Between 1880 and 1890 commercial production of inexpensive rolled-steel structural shapes became general and the new low-priced steel soon began to displace iron in bridge building. Since there is no readily visible difference between iron and steel trusses and since the principles of design and construction are identical, this change became simply a matter of altering the basis of calculations to allow for the greater strength of the steel.

The first use of steel in truss construction was made in 1869–1874, several years before the low-priced steel was available. For alloy steel tubes were used in build-

FIG. 21.—Historic Menai Suspension Bridge, constructed by Telford and opened in 1826.

FIG. 22.—Fribourg Suspension Bridge was the first carried by wire instead of chains.

Fig. 23.—The great Elbe River bridges at Hamburg.

FIG. 24.—Building the world's first all-steel bridge at Glasgow, Missouri, in 1879.

FIG. 25.—Brooklyn Bridge represented one of the great achievements in bridge building.

ing the arch trusses of the Eads Bridge over the Mississippi River at St. Louis. These tubes, it might be noted, were of chromium steel and represented only one of several innovations in the construction of this interesting bridge, of which we shall say more elsewhere. A few years later, the availability of the new low-priced steel led to the construction of the first all-steel truss bridge—marking the beginning of the end for iron bridges and the start of our modern era.

Chapter VI
The Steel Era Begins

Four Bridges That Made History.

IN THE last third of the nineteenth century, four bridges
were built that served largely to inaugurate the modern
era of steel bridges. Taking these in chronological order
of completion they were: Capt. James B. Eads's steel
arch bridge over the Mississippi River at St. Louis;
Gen. Sooy Smith's all-steel truss bridge over the
Missouri River at Glasgow; the great Brooklyn suspension bridge of the Roeblings at New York; and the
gigantic cantilever bridge of Sir John Fowler and Sir
Benjamin Baker over the Firth of Forth in Scotland.

Although we have already mentioned the use of steel
eyebars in a Vienna suspension bridge of 1828, the use
of steel tube members in the Eads Bridge is generally
accepted as marking the beginning of the steel age in
bridge building. Contrary to a rather prevalent impression, however, the Eads is not an all-steel bridge. Iron
was used in conjunction with the alloy steel tubes in its
arch trusses. This bridge was completed in 1874 after
about five years of arduous work and heartbreaking construction difficulties. It is a double-deck structure, the
upper deck extending over the full width of the bridge

82

and carrying a highway and sidewalks, while the lower deck carries two lines of railroad tracks, one between each pair of outer trusses. The center span of the bridge is 520 feet and there are two side spans of 502 feet each in the clear.

The structure is of historic interest for several reasons. Not only does it represent the first use of steel in truss-bridge construction but it was, besides, the longest fixed-end metal arch and, together with the Brooklyn Bridge, was one of the first two bridges in which pneumatic caissons were applied to pier construction in this country. The caisson marked a most important advance in deep-water pier construction and its first large-scale use in bridge building was on the Chepstow Viaduct in England in 1843 to 1851. The principle we shall describe later in our chapter on The Foundation Builders' Job. The arches of the Eads Bridge are constructed of chrome steel tubes assembled to form upper and lower "chords," or continuous members, of its arch trusses and these tubes are held in position by a latticework of diagonals to complete the truss. Each arch truss is rigidly secured to the piers at its ends instead of being hinged, as in more recent designs.

One might well have expected the railroads to welcome the Eads Bridge but, on the contrary, they did not take kindly to the innovation. Like only too many important new enterprises, it was an engineering success which was to become a financial failure. For months after its completion, the roads continued to ferry their cars over the river and the bridge company, a private enterprise, was finally forced into bankruptcy. Eventually, the railroads were able to obtain its use on their own terms and the historic structure still remains in service.

The First All-steel Bridge.

From records of the old Chicago and Alton Railroad, now a part of the great Baltimore and Ohio Railroad system, comes an interesting story of the first all-steel bridge. In 1878, when railroad construction was still proceeding at a rapid pace in less developed parts of the United States, the Chicago and Alton began construction of a line between Kansas City and Mexico, Missouri. In the course of this project it became necessary to bridge the Missouri River at Glasgow and the Company engaged Gen. William Sooy Smith to make the surveys and to supervise the construction of the bridge. With its total length of 2,700-odd feet, the proposed bridge represented a considerable undertaking for that period and thus created fairly general interest.

At about the same time, A. T. Hay of Burlington, Iowa, was bringing to a successful conclusion his experiments with steel manufacture and had just perfected a process for making commercially an inexpensive steel which he was marketing under the name of "Hay steel." It was beginning to look as if all of Hay's work had been in vain, for with the exception of Eads's expensive alloy steel tubes, designers of metal truss bridges were

84

still using wrought or cast iron and all looked askance upon the new low-priced steel. Like too many other inventors, Hay wore out considerable shoe leather while trying to interest people in his steel. Finally he succeeded in obtaining a hearing from Gen. Sooy Smith, who was sufficiently openminded to agree that he would investigate the material. Tests were made and upon their conclusion, Sooy Smith announced that his bridge was going to be of steel.

When the news was given out that his new Glasgow bridge was to be made wholly of the new cheap steel, General Smith suddenly found that he had stirred up a hornet's nest. A cry of alarm arose. For, although the Eads Bridge was built partly of steel, this was still considered a more or less untried material and people were particularly suspicious of the new lower-priced steel. Even those who should have been the most capable judges, bridge builders among them, protested against the risks involved in constructing a bridge of the new material. It would be too rigid to withstand vibration of trains, the steel would become brittle and break in cold weather—these were some of the objections raised.

History does not record all that was said at the time but, if his opponents ran true to form in such cases, we can picture them arguing that iron was good enough for their fathers and it was good enough for them. What history *does* record, and what is much more to the point, is that the bridge was really built, despite the calamity howlers. Apparently few others than Gen. Sooy Smith,

Mr. Hay and the Chicago and Alton really expected that the bridge would stand up. By 1879 it was ready, having been erected in the then surprisingly short time of about one year. This epoch-making structure consisted of five steel-truss spans, each almost 315 feet long, with approaches consisting of iron trestles and plate girders but including also two 140-foot trusses.

Eventually, it turned out, the bridge did come down, but only after the growth of the Chicago and Alton's traffic and the increased weight of later rolling stock made it necessary to replace the old spans with others of heavier construction in 1902! And when the old steel trusses were dismantled after all those years of faithful service, they showed not the slightest justification for the dire predictions that had been made nearly a quarter of a century earlier. By this time, bridge designers had long since come to look askance upon any member of their profession proposing to construct a bridge of *iron!*

Brooklyn Bridge, a Mark in Bridge History.

While Sooy Smith was putting the finishing touches to his new bridge, two other pioneers were already at work establishing a record that was to remain for many years the high point in suspension-bridge construction. John A. Roebling, designer of the momentous Brooklyn Bridge, did not live to see his work much more than started. Actual construction began in 1869 and he died in the same year. Erection of the bridge was carried on to its successful completion under the direction of his son, Washington A. Roebling, and was opened to traffic in 1883, crossing the wide East River channel from New York City to Brooklyn with a single span of 1,595½ feet.

This bridge represents a gigantic advance over every previous structure, regardless of the type, and it incorporated many important innovations in suspension-bridge work. The suspension system consists of four steel-wire cables made up of parallel wires formed into circular shape and wrapped on the outside with steel wire for protection against weather. This new method of construction has since become generally used for large suspension bridges. The cables are carried upon stone towers reaching a height of 275 feet above high-water level, while the mid-river clearance under the span is 133 feet. The bridge has a single deck totaling eighty-six feet in width but divided to provide for two elevated railroad tracks, two trolley car tracks, a single lane roadway beside each trolley track, and a central footwalk of fifteen feet.

Strange though it may seem to us in these days of great bridges, there was considerable opposition to the Brooklyn Bridge project when it was first proposed by its designer. That may have been due in part to the inherent conservatism with which larger cities are inclined to consider such radical innovations. Perhaps it was not entirely divorced from the "vested interests" of the period as represented by some old-established ferries. Whatever the cause, there is no gainsaying the fact that

87

opposition delayed for several years the realization of Roebling's dream.

While the opposing forces still remained in control, it happened that the winter of 1866–1867 turned out to be one of the severest in many a year. Indeed, it was one of those that we are inclined to call a "good, old-fashioned winter," even though the Weather Bureau records do show little or no change in our climate over a long period of time. In any case, this particular winter brought chaos and stagnation to East River traffic by virtually tying up the ferries forming the sole means of transportation between New York and Brooklyn. History has it that some travelers from the 150-mile-distant city of Albany were able to reach downtown New York before those who had started at the same time from the neighbor city directly across the river! One can well imagine how this development threw a monkey wrench into the machinery of the opposition. So, as it usually does, irrefutable logic finally won out and work began in 1867 with the incorporation of the New York Bridge Company to build the structure for the two cities.

Actual construction began in 1869, within a short time after the organization of the company, and from that time on the elder Roebling devoted practically every waking hour of his life to the project. This was not destined to be long for, while at work on the site of the Brooklyn tower, he met with an accident which resulted in his death in the same year. His son Washington A. Roebling immediately took over direction and, as we have already noted, eventually carried it through to success although he, in turn, sacrificed his health to the project. Fire broke out in one of the compressed-air caissons, which in those days were built of wood instead of steel as in later years. Young Roebling took personal charge of the fire fighting, remaining in the chamber under pressure for about twenty-four hours without a break. The terrific experience left him an invalid for life and, although he continued to direct the work, his office had to be at his bedside thereafter.

Despite discouraging problems, the foundations were completed and great stone towers soon began to rear their way towards the sky. Almost terrifying in height they seemed in those days before the advent of modern skyscrapers. By April of 1877, the first of the suspension wires had been strung from anchorage to anchorage over the tops of the towers and the wide expanse of river. Wire by wire, the cables grew until the last wire was added in October of the following year. They seemed like giants, the four great cables each measuring almost sixteen inches in diameter! Though they look puny beside the much greater cables of recent bridges, the Brooklyn Bridge cables represent one of the greatest advances in bridge engineering history. They carry a much longer span than any that had been previously built, and they also stand as the first example of the application of *steel wire* to bridge construction. The wire cables of earlier bridges had been made of iron wires. In this bridge, also, for the first time galvanizing

89

was used as a means of protecting wire employed for bridge suspension.

Construction proceeded steadily. We might think it slow progress as judged by later standards, but Roebling had to meet and to solve his problems as he went. He was engaged upon a work practically without precedent. And not all of his problems had to do with engineering. As Gustav Lindenthal very pointedly noted in a review of bridge development, great pressure was brought to bear upon the bridge engineers by a few of the city politicians. Since the bridge was being built by use of public funds, some of these gentlemen developed a practice of sending around several hundred men to be added to the pay roll just before each election. Not knowing what to do with such inexperienced help, the engineers had no choice but to keep them loafing around and idling away their time without even a pretense of working! This, Lindenthal pointed out, might well be counted as one of the reasons why Brooklyn Bridge cost nearly twice as much as estimated and took so many years to complete.

Finally, however, the great bridge was finished after about thirteen or fourteen years of continuous labors, and the span was opened to pedestrians and road vehicles in May of 1883. By September of the same year, shuttle-train elevated railway service was put into operation. It was not until the beginning of 1908 that through train service began, earlier passengers being required to change cars at the Brooklyn terminus.

90

The Forth Bridge—a Masterpiece of Engineering.

History was made rapidly in those early days of steel bridges. While Roebling was still hard at work upon his East River bridge, two other engineers were starting construction of a bridge that was to rank as one of the greatest engineering structures of all time. This was the gigantic Forth Bridge, a cantilever structure designed by Sir John Fowler and Sir Benjamin Baker, two eminent engineers of the period. Opened in 1889, it represented so tremendous an advance that for nearly three decades of rapid development in bridge construction it remained the longest span bridge in the world. Even at this date it has the second longest span of all cantilever bridges yet built. While its cost of $16,135,000, including approaches, does not seem great beside recent bridge costs, it was a stupendous sum for that time.

The Forth Bridge consists of two main cantilever spans, each with a suspended truss in the center, a side span at each end, and fifteen approach trusses of lesser interest. The two main spans each measure 1,710 feet and at their centers are 152 feet above the water, while the structures on each pier rise to a height of 343 feet above the water. The whole bridge design embodies some radically independent ideas in bridge construction, many of which have never been duplicated elsewhere. Most of the main compression members of the structure are of tubular form and some conception of the massive proportions of the structure may be gained from the fact that certain of these tubes are as much as twelve feet in diameter. The tubes are formed of curved plates riveted together and fastened to internal stiffening frames.

This built-up tubular form has the distinction of never having been applied to bridge construction either before or since and it represents a distinctly novel departure in framing a structure of such size. However, experience showed that though the resulting structure is very efficient, its fabrication is not economical. Hence, it is not likely to be used again.

The bridge is built mainly of Siemens-Martin steel and at the time of its construction, as well as for many years thereafter, it was regarded as one of the engineering wonders of the world. With its great spans and its total length of 8,300 feet (including approaches), the Forth Bridge became to the advocates of cantilever construction what the Brooklyn Bridge was to those favoring the suspension type. In engineering importance, however, it might be ranked above the Brooklyn Bridge —not so much for its somewhat larger span as for its great rigidity and tremendous strength. For the Forth Bridge carries two lines of trains and its designers incorporated in its structure an excess of strength which makes it equal to carrying heavy modern trains, even though they are permitted to pass each other at high speed in the center of its spans. This fine compliment to its designers can be the better appreciated if we point out that trains are required to slow down when crossing many bridges of much more recent construction!

Chapter VII
Modern Steel Truss Bridges

===

The First Quebec Bridge.

IT WAS not until the year 1900 that the Forth Bridge record was threatened and the first competitor was, as was proved later, to end in one of the worst bridge disasters of history. The occasion was the first attempt to bridge the great St. Lawrence River at Quebec. A great cantilever structure had been designed and work upon it began in 1900.

The design for that first Quebec Bridge—a totally different structure from the present one—called for a central span of 1,800 feet from center to center of the main piers. Since it would be the first to exceed Fowler and Baker's gigantic Forth Bridge, the project excited much comment. Unfortunately, however, the whole undertaking started under a very serious handicap, the available funds falling short of those really necessary. While we know this *now*, the allotted figure seemed practicable at the time and the bridge designers made every effort to reduce the amount of steel in order to keep down the cost of their structure.

That they went too far was not evident until a few

hours before startling headlines in the evening papers of August 29, 1907, fairly shrieked the story of the bridge's collapse while under construction. Among bridge accidents of recent times, the collapse was second only to the Tay Bridge disaster in loss of life. In material losses it was even greater. Coming at so late a date as 1907, it seemed, in the light of engineering knowledge, less excusable, and hence caused a furore in the engineering profession. All had assumed that approval of the design by one of the most prominent bridge engineers afforded full insurance against such a calamity.

First warnings of impending disaster came a few days before the failure, when some of the lower chord members showed signs of buckling under their load. Indeed, this condition at once became a matter of concern to the engineers and they had just decided to suspend work pending investigation when news of the collapse reached them. Eighty-six men were at work on the huge south cantilever of the bridge when that great steel framework collapsed into a tangled mass of folded steel. Only eleven of the men escaped with their lives, one making a wild dash of 300 feet along the anchor span of the toppling cantilever. Even as he ran, the structure was sinking beneath his feet and he had to jump to safety over a rapidly opening gap at the south approach. One eyewitness said that the whole framework collapsed by sinking down like "ice pillars whose ends were rapidly melting away."

An immediate investigation was undertaken by the

Canadian Government to determine the cause of the collapse and to ensure its elimination from a later design. In the report of its findings the investigating body laid bare the excessive lengths to which weight reduction had been carried and recommended construction of a new and heavier design. Other engineers were engaged to carry out the plans and work was started upon the present bridge, which was opened several years later and which now carries the tracks of the Canadian National Railways over the St. Lawrence at the same point.

The new structure is, as we have said, a totally different bridge from the one that collapsed. Excepting that its span is the same, 1,800 feet, the new bridge has little in common with the first one. Indeed, the comparison between the two designs becomes startling when one learns that the present bridge was designed for the same load as the first, yet for its construction nearly two and one-half times as much steel was required! But the bridge builders' troubles were not over with rectification of the faulty design and it once seemed as though the St. Lawrence was doomed to remain unbridged at Quebec. For another serious accident occurred to delay completion of the new structure although, this time, reflecting no discredit upon either designers or builders. While the central suspended span of the new bridge was being lifted into place everything was proceeding smoothly and according to schedule. Indeed, some of the visiting executive engineers, after watching the proceedings for a while, decided that this would be an appropriate time

95

to go for their lunch. Suddenly a steel casting, which had appeared sound and trustworthy, snapped without warning and one of the corner rocker supports upset. Which occurred first is still a moot question. The 5,200-ton span which was being lifted dropped into the river and was lost, carrying some workers with it. This time eleven workers paid the penalty of man's temerity in bridging great rivers.

Eventually a new central span was erected and this time the lifting into place was completed successfully and the bridge was opened to service in 1917. Since then it has been in regular use, carrying trains of the Canadian National Railways over the river. The completion of the Quebec Bridge at last took away from the Forth Bridge its record as the longest span cantilever. During the intervening period between the two bridges and since the completion of the Quebec Bridge, numerous cantilevers have been built throughout the world. But the Quebec Bridge still retains the record for cantilever spans.

Queensboro Bridge.

Although not even approaching the Forth and Quebec bridges in span, the Queensboro Bridge at New York City is of interest as being one of the largest bridges built from the point of view of capacity. It is a cantilever structure crossing the East River from Manhattan to Long Island City by way of Welfare Island—an island situated almost in the middle of the

96

FIG. 26.—The gigantic Forth Bridge, one of the greatest engineering feats of all time. (*Photograph by Ewing Galloway.*)

FIG. 27.—Quebec Bridge has the longest span of any cantilever type.

FIG. 28.—Newark Bay Lift Bridge of the New Jersey Central Railroad.

FIG. 29.—Queensboro Bridge over the East River, New York.

FIG. 30.—Pulaski Skyway, a great aerial highway connecting Newark with Jersey City.

FIG. 31.—Danish Little Belt Bridge.

river at that point. The structure, completed in 1909, was designed under the direction of Gustav Lindenthal, then Commissioner of Bridges of the City of New York, but best known as designer of the Hell Gate Bridge.

The Queensboro Bridge has two main cantilever spans, one being 1,182 feet and the other 984 feet, with a connecting span of 630 feet between them and anchor spans of 469 and 459 feet at the ends. The bridge is double-decked, with the upper deck carrying two elevated railway tracks, one twenty-two-and-a-half-foot roadway and a nine-and-three-quarter-foot sidewalk. The lower deck carries two streetcar tracks and a fifty-one-foot roadway. Queensboro Bridge has the distinction of being the first bridge in which nickel steel was used extensively, the top chord eyebars and their pins being of this material while the rest of the structure is of medium carbon steel.

While cantilever and suspension bridges have been growing to spans far exceeding those of the "simple truss" and "continuous truss" bridges, these types have not remained unprogressive, although they have not been sharing the limelight with their competitors. Both the length of span and the carrying capacity of simple truss bridges have been constantly increased since the days of Bollman's Harper's Ferry Bridge and Sooy Smith's Glasgow Bridge. We now have simple trusses that range in size up to the 720-foot span, designed by Ralph Modjeski and constructed across the Ohio River at Metropolis, Illinois, and the 716-foot span, designed by Harrington-Howard and Ash and built across the same river at Paducah, Kentucky.

From the simple truss there was soon evolved the "continuous" truss, which is substantially a series of trusses resting upon a chain of piers, with the abutting ends of the trusses each rigidly secured to one another. The trusses, in other words, have been connected to form one continuous structure instead of ending at each intermediate support. This construction provides both greater rigidity and greater strength and hence is used where the spans become too great for a series of simple trusses. The Sciotoville Bridge, carrying a branch of the Chesapeake and Ohio Railway over the Ohio River, is a truss of the continuous type. It still holds the record of having the longest spans of its type, each of its two spans measuring 775 feet from pier to pier. This bridge was designed by Gustav Lindenthal and was completed in 1916.

Three Miles of Aerial Highway.

Stretching its great length across the Jersey Meadows from Jersey City towards the nearby city of Newark, New Jersey, and resembling a giant roller coaster, is the Pulaski Skyway, an aerial highway which was opened to traffic in 1932. The Skyway was named after Count Casimir Pulaski, a Polish soldier and major general in the American Revolutionary Army. This unique structure, consisting of a whole series of cantilever bridges, was built as part of the highway projects of the state of New Jersey and is under direction of the State Highway Department. It forms one of the links in that state's super highway, Route Number 25, running from the Hudson River to the Delaware River and forming a major link in the highway system along the Atlantic coast. The entire structure of the Skyway includes about three miles of high-level steelwork, most of it being of cantilever trusses. Two 550-foot cantilever spans are used in crossing the Hackensack and Passaic rivers at a height of 135 feet to permit the passage of ocean vessels.

The recurrence of earthquakes has always been a problem for designers of structures in certain parts of the world where these occur. Since the location of the Carquinez Strait Bridge in California was within such an area its designers had one extra problem to worry about. The possibility of an earthquake's damaging their structure inspired them to make some provision for breaking the force of the quake and resulted in certain innovations in bridge design when the span was erected. Six great hydraulic buffers are placed at the expansion joints of this bridge to check horizontal vibrations or sudden movements resulting from shocks and the stress calculations included allowances based upon the records of the force of previous earthquakes. Its designers have never yet had the opportunity of observing how the plan works out in practice, but the news of an earthquake in that area—if ever it should occur—would be read with very keen interest by bridge designers.

99

Bridging the Little Belt in Denmark.

The Danish State Railways has recently completed (in 1935) an interesting project which included spanning the Little Belt Straits by a high-level bridge of the steel truss type, to carry both rail and highway traffic. This project became one of considerable magnitude, for the moderate height of adjacent territory required extensive approach construction to bring the bridge floor up to the high level necessary for a bridge which had to clear ocean vessels, while the channel conditions required long spans for each portion.

The bridge proper consists of five main spans of steel trusses which are connected to form one continuous truss, extending from shore to shore. The total length of the truss is 2,700 feet and the central span, largest of the five, is 720 feet. Clearance under this span is 108 feet over the water. At each end of the steel truss bridge is a series of high concrete arches of the open-spandrel type, a form which we will describe in detail in the chapter, Reinforced Concrete Bridges. These arches serve to carry the railways and roadways up to the bridge level, while extensive embankments form the final connecting link between the arches and the ground level.

In the opening pages we mentioned that the great bridge crossing San Francisco Bay, among its other spectacular features, possesses the distinction of having a cantilever span that is exceeded only by those of the Forth and Quebec Bridges. This Bay Bridge cantilever has a central span of 1,400 feet and side spans of 508

100

and 512 feet, as compared with the 1,710-foot cantilevers of the Forth Bridge and the 1,800-foot span of the Quebec Bridge. Unlike these two bridges, however, the Bay Bridge is double decked. The upper deck carries a fifty-eight-foot roadway for six lanes of passenger vehicles while the lower deck carries a thirty-one-foot roadway for three lanes of commercial vehicles and two tracks for interurban rapid transit trains. Connecting the cantilever section of the bridge with Oakland is a long steel structure that consists of nineteen simple trusses ranging in span from 291 to 509 feet. The lower deck of the cantilever main span is 192 feet above high water and the clearance underneath is 185 feet. The total length of the entire East Bay crossing structure is 19,400 feet as against the 8,300 feet of the Forth Bridge main structure. The whole project has many other interesting features, some of which we have already mentioned while others we shall describe later in connection with the great suspension spans that form the West Bay section of this bridge.

Chapter VIII

Arches Become Symphonies
in Steel

The Hell Gate Bridge.

OF ALL the structures designed by the late Gustav Lindenthal, probably no other is quite so well known and so universally commented upon as his Hell Gate Bridge, connecting Long Island with the Borough of the Bronx and providing direct rail connection between the Pennsylvania and New Haven railroads. The whole project really includes three other spans and a considerable length of viaduct in addition to the actual span crossing the Hell Gate itself; but the rest of the long structure is so dwarfed by the big arch spanning that arm of the East River that people have come to think of this alone when the work is mentioned. So the official name, "New York Connecting Railway," is generally dropped in favor of the more popular—if less accurate—title, "Hell Gate Bridge." Indeed, even in the advertising matter of the railroads themselves, this part of their lines becomes the Hell Gate Route because of the general interest attached to the bridge.

All of the interest is deserved, for the Hell Gate arch

102

is not only one of the heaviest and longest steel arches ever built, but at the same time one of the most beautiful steel bridges ever constructed. The big steel arch with its massive abutments and its gracefully sweeping lines, carrying the tracks 140 feet above the river, forms a striking picture that has long since become one of the sights of foremost interest in the metropolitan area. Its span of 977½ feet made it the longest steel arch in the world from its completion in 1917 until the Bayonne Bridge and the Sydney Harbour Bridge were opened in 1931 and 1932.

The Hell Gate Bridge proper forms one link in a short line owned jointly by the Pennsylvania and New Haven railroads. It was constructed to provide these roads with a through route between points north and south of the City of New York. The entire development includes several miles of cutting and filling, as well as a considerable number of smaller bridges over highways and other railroads. The approaches include about three miles of viaduct construction of the concrete-pier-and-plate-girder type, while the other bridges that are dwarfed by the Hell Gate arch include a four-span truss crossing from Wards Island to Randalls Island and a two-span truss bridge from the latter island to the Bronx. The striking curves of the Hell Gate arch did not result entirely from artistic considerations, since they were largely necessitated by the rigidity and clearance requirements of a structure designed to carry heavy steel trains hauled by powerful locomotives.

103

Bayonne Bridge, the World's Longest Arch.

As we have said before, bridge records are short lived. The official opening of the Bayonne Bridge over Kill Van Kull from Bayonne, New Jersey, to Staten Island, New York, in 1931 took from the Hell Gate Bridge its record as the longest steel arch, although it still kept its record as the then heaviest steel-arch bridge. The new bridge brought the figure up to 1,652 feet between the hinges of its great steel arch, supporting a roadway at a clear height of 150 feet above the water at the center of the span. Unlike Hell Gate, however, the Bayonne Bridge carries a highway instead of a railroad and it forms one of several interstate crossings constructed and operated by a joint body of the two states in connection with the development and coordination of transportation facilities within the port area.

Between this bridge as the longest span arch in the world and the George Washington Bridge as, for several years, the longest span of any kind in the world, a peculiar coincidence exists, for both were designed by the same engineer, O. H. Ammann, and both are operated under the same ownership—that of the Port of New York Authority. In its initial stage, the Bayonne Bridge provides a forty-foot roadway for a total of four lanes of traffic and it has also a sidewalk. The bridge is so constructed that two rapid transit railway tracks, or an additional twenty-five feet width of roadway for two or three more lanes, may be added in the future.

Sydney Harbour Bridge, Widest Long Span in the World.

By a strange coincidence, due to labor troubles which delayed its erection, the 1,650-foot Sydney Harbour Bridge was under construction at the same time as the Bayonne Bridge. Thus came about the unusual circumstance of the simultaneous erection of two record-breaking steel-arch bridges almost equal in size but located on opposite sides of the globe. In recognition of the coincidence, arrangements were made to use the same pair of gold shears for cutting the ribbons that symbolized the opening of each of the two bridges, one in the United States and the other in Australia. This prized implement is now in possession of The Port of New York Authority, having first been used in opening the Bayonne Bridge in November of 1931 and then sent halfway around the world to serve the same purpose for the Sydney Harbour ceremonies in March of 1932. Later, it was returned to the owners.

The Sydney Harbour Bridge has the characteristic appearance that is common to some others of the steel-arch type. It differs from these mainly in its gigantic size; for not only is it a bridge of great span, but it holds the record of being the heaviest arch bridge and the widest long bridge of any kind in the world. This great structure carries, all on one level, four lines of electric railway tracks, a six-lane vehicular roadway, and two ten-foot sidewalks, making the startling total of 160 feet in width! The great arch towers 440 feet above the harbor and the roadway structure clears the water by 170 feet in the center of its span.

Construction began in 1924 and the bridge was opened in March of 1932, the work, as we have already stated, having been delayed by labor troubles. Its actual construction really involved only about six years. Including the approaches, this bridge is about two-and-three-quarters miles long and its construction (again including the approaches, as well as all other costs) came to about $45,000,000. The entire structure required some 52,300 tons of steel, of which about 37,000 tons went into the gigantic arch. The general plan of the bridge was laid down by Dr. J. J. C. Bradfield, Chief Engineer of the Public Works Department of the New South Wales Government, while the bridge structure was designed by Ralph Freeman, consulting engineer for Dorman, Long and Company, Ltd., its builders. Resembling the Hell Gate arch in general appearance, this bridge also makes a fine appearance to the eye with the sweeping lines of its arch truss and the two massive stone-faced towers that form the abutments.

Chapter IX

Modern Suspension Bridges

DESIGNERS of bridges are unanimous in their agreement that the suspension type permits attainment of greater span than is possible with any other form of construction. Yet from 1889 until the opening of the Ambassador Bridge in 1928, we find a strange paradox persisting in that the cantilever type of bridge, represented first by the Forth Bridge and later by the Quebec Bridge, held the "longest span" record for all types. While this is apparently puzzling at first, the explanation is simple. It was formerly believed that a suspension bridge could not be made sufficiently rigid to carry heavy concentrated loads. Each of these two long-span bridges was built to carry heavy railroad trains and, hence, it had to possess a high degree of rigidity. Thus the flexibility then considered unavoidable in the suspension type led to its being discarded in favor of the supposedly more rigid, if heavier, cantilever type.

Within more recent years, there came a wave of construction of long-span bridges which were designed to carry highway traffic and some also for the lighter interurban or rapid transit trains. The lesser weight of this traffic, combined with the greater stiffness of suspension bridges of very long span, worked toward bringing this type of construction into favor. Furthermore, advances in the design of suspension bridges have made it possible to incorporate in them almost any degree of rigidity which may be desired. So it has happened that no cantilever bridge built since has exceeded the 1,800-foot span of the Quebec Bridge of 1917. In the meantime, successive bridges of the suspension type continued to increase in size until eventually they passed, and soon after greatly exceeded, the span of our biggest cantilever structures.

The first suspension bridge to exceed the old Brooklyn Bridge span was the 1,600-foot Williamsburgh Bridge over the East River at New York, completed in 1903, almost within the shadow of the earlier bridge. The Bear Mountain Bridge, in 1924, added to this figure another thirty-two feet, although it is a much smaller bridge from the point of view of carrying capacity. It remained for the Delaware River Bridge (in 1926) to become the first suspension structure exceeding the span of the then thirty-seven-year-old Forth Bridge, although even this structure did not approach the Forth Bridge in over-all length, nor—for that matter—did it equal the Quebec Bridge in span.

Spanning the Delaware River.

With the opening of this Delaware River Bridge, a century-old dream became a reality. It has been called a "second Brooklyn Bridge" due to the similarity of connecting two large cities which formerly had been dependent upon ferries. Early in the history of Philadelphia, a ferry began operating across the Delaware River and almost a hundred years ago some visionaries began to think of bridging this expanse of water. Several times projects were advanced for construction of a bridge but it was 1919 before any came within sight of attaining their ends. In that year the state of Pennsylvania and the state of New Jersey appointed a joint commission to look into the possibility of bridging the river and from then on the project moved steadily ahead. By 1921 the investigating board of engineers had reported favorably; by the following year the bridge had been designed by Ralph Modjeski and its construction was under way; by the end of 1922 caissons for the pier foundations had been sunk to their final position, resting upon bedrock as much as 105 feet below high water. The work continued steadily, following a schedule that called for its completion in time for Philadelphia's Sesquicentennial Exposition of 1926. The bridge was opened for traffic on the first of July of that year, just three days before the sesquicentennial of the signing of the Declaration of Independence, with which Philadelphia has been so closely associated in history.

This "Camden Bridge," as it is often called, although its official title is "Delaware River Bridge," is of the cable suspension type with a span of 1,750 feet, thus exceeding the Forth Bridge span by forty feet and being, as we have said, the first of its type to surpass it.

At mean high water the bridge has a clearance underneath of 135 feet, about the same as that of New York's East River bridges. Its roadway is fifty-seven feet wide and on each side of it there is space for two rapid transit railway tracks, making a total floor width of 128 feet. Some of these tracks have been installed and trains from Philadelphia now operate across the bridge into Camden. The steel towers extend 380 feet above the water and the two great suspension cables are each thirty inches in diameter, being exceeded only by the thirty-six-inch cables of the George Washington Bridge and the thirty-six-and-a-half-inch cables of the Golden Gate Bridge.

In the rapidly moving record of engineering achievement many bridge builders have found that the distinction attached to their work by reason of superior size may be short lived. No sooner is a new record made than we hear the "rat-a-tat-tat" of pneumatic hammers in the hands of riveters engaged on a still larger bridge. This certainly has been true in a number of cases within the busy period of the last twenty years and the Delaware River Bridge was no exception.

Just about two years after its opening another structure was completed to take from it the longest span title, although leaving with it (for the time being) certain distinctions in the way of cable size and over-all width. The newer bridge was the 1,850-foot Ambassador Bridge over the Detroit River, connecting the city of that name with the Canadian border cities of Windsor and Sandwich. In addition to becoming the longest span suspension bridge, the Ambassador also exceeded the span of the Quebec cantilever bridge thus, for the first time in many years, wresting the "longest span" record from the cantilever type. Designed (with the collaboration of Modjeski, Masters and Chase as consultants) by the Engineering Department of McClintic-Marshall Company, its builders, this bridge carries a forty-seven-foot roadway and an eight-foot sidewalk across the river. No provision for rapid transit railroads is included. Its towers extend 363 feet above the water and clearance under the bridge in midriver is 152 feet. Side spans are carried by trusses instead of being suspended from the main cables, as in most bridges of the kind.

One unusual feature of this bridge is due to the fact that it connects two countries. This circumstance made it necessary to provide stations for customs inspection at each end. All cars crossing are given a quick examination and if satisfactory are immediately cleared and allowed to enter the country for which they are headed. If the customs officials have reason to question the contents or occupants of any car, it is directed out of the traffic lane into a detention space provided for that purpose. The car and its occupants are then subjected to a more thorough examination without delaying others.

George Washington Bridge.

The George Washington Bridge at New York City, from 1931 until completion of the new Golden Gate

111

Bridge at San Francisco, held the record of having the world's longest span. In one step, this gigantic structure inaugurated a new order of magnitude in bridges, almost doubling the longest span previously built. It represents the ultimate realization of a dream that practical bridge designers in all parts of the world have had in their minds for at least fifty years—for talk of bridging the Hudson at New York began to be heard just about the time that Roebling went to work on his historic East River bridge to Brooklyn.

Many Hudson River bridging projects appeared in the years that followed, the earlier ones contemplating a bridge from the downtown section of New York City. Later projects moved the site progressively farther up town and the opening of the Holland Tunnel apparently put a definite end to all thoughts of a downtown bridge. Sites at Canal Street, 23d Street, 57th Street and other locations were considered, in turn, by the promoters of various bridge projects. Earlier plans were for exclusively rail projects or a combination of rail and road with the former dominating. The development of automobiles changed many things within the short space of twenty-five years and it completely altered most of the Hudson River bridge plans.

Best known of these earlier projects was Gustav Lindenthal's plan to bridge the river at 23d Street. Subsequent developments caused him to change the site to 57th Street but the gigantic size of his project interfered with its financing and thus prevented its realiza-

FIG. 32.—Bayonne Bridge, the longest steel arch ever built.

FIG. 33.—New York Connecting Railway bridges, before construction of the Triborough Bridge. (*Photograph by Fairchild Aerial Camera Corporation.*)

Fig. 34.—Delaware River Bridge connecting Camden and Philadelphia.

FIG. 35.—The George Washington Bridge inaugurated a new scale of size.

tion. In the meantime, construction of the Holland Tunnel and the George Washington Bridge put a virtual end to further progress of the 57th Street project. So it thus happened that the first bridge to cross the Hudson at New York City was the George Washington Bridge at 178th Street.

Conception of this bridge originated with O. H. Ammann, a former associate of Lindenthal's, who succeeded in convincing the Port of New York Authority that his project was economically sound. With the endorsement of both states, and to a certain extent also with the weight of their financial support behind it, the financing which had been found insuperable for other projects became a practicability for Ammann's bridge. The tremendous size of the undertaking and its estimated cost of nearly $60,000,000, dwarfed by comparison every bridge previously built. Hence, it was necessary to conduct an exceptionally thorough investigation of construction conditions, cost and possible toll revenues before work was actually undertaken. These surveys showed not only that such a bridge could be built and financed, but also that it was needed and that it would be economically justified. Construction began in 1927 and such had been the advancement in bridge engineering that, despite its great size, the Hudson River bridge was opened in October of 1931, after less than four and a half years of actual work.

This great bridge has a main span of 3,500 feet from tower to tower, with end spans of 650 and 610 feet, making the total length of the main bridge 4,760 feet. The finished structure, with its prospective lower deck added, will have a clearance of 213 feet over midriver. Its enormous weight is carried by four thirty-six-inch cables, each consisting of 26,474 parallel wires that run from anchorage to anchorage over gigantic towers reaching 635 feet above the water. On the New Jersey side an anchorage was constructed by drilling into the solid rock of the Palisades; at the New York end it was necessary to build a virtual mountain of concrete with sufficient weight to resist the pull of the four great cables. Ultimate arrangement of the bridge provided for an eight-lane roadway on the upper (or present) deck with four rapid transit railroad tracks, or a second roadway, on the prospective lower deck. Such is the ultimate capacity of this bridge that the Port of New York Authority, its builder and operator, estimates the maximum traffic which it can normally handle as being 30,000,000 vehicle-crossings per year. Despite a cost of $54,857,000, in its present stage of completion, this bridge was so much needed that in the first full year of operation its earnings covered all operating expense, interest and amortization.

Construction of the George Washington Bridge required about 100,000 tons of steel without counting the additional material which will be needed to complete its prospective lower deck. Almost 1,000,000 rivets were used in the towers and its four great cables contain a total of 105,000 miles of wire—enough to make four circles around the earth! The tower foundations extend down to bedrock far below the river bed, one part of the New Jersey piers being seventy-six feet below water. In constructing the New Jersey approach and the anchorage, which is drilled into the Palisades traprock, 300,000 cubic yards of rock had to be excavated. This represented so large a job that the contractor installed a complete stone-crushing plant at the site and went into the business of selling broken stone while the excavating was going on. The New York anchorage is a gigantic block that took enough stone, sand and cement to construct a small town. Even the approaches in themselves constituted a job of no mean size. Including the real estate which had to be acquired, approaches for the two ends of the bridge cost no less than $18,785,000 in cold cash. The roadway over the bridge represented a job so substantial that the contractor purchased two narrow-gauge electric locomotives and trains of dump cars merely for the purpose of transporting concrete from his mixing plant on the New York side out to working points on the structure! The towers had to be so large that the top of each measures 50 by 180 feet, an area almost equaling that of five city building lots.

Wire Rope Bridges.

The cable bridges which we have just described are all supported by steel wires which are laid parallel to form great cables, the completed cable being wrapped for protection. A type of suspension which is not new but

115

which has recently become more popular, makes use of "twisted-strand cables," in place of the individual wires. In this system, strands formed of twisted wires are made up in the shop complete with their end fastenings and all ready to lay in place. In the fabrication of these strands, they are measured and cut while under tension and their end sockets are applied, after which they are "pre-stressed" by the application of a temporary load in the shop. This operation takes out most of the stretch and eliminates danger of excessive stretching after the bridge is put into service. The system has been used in a number of recent bridges such as the one built at Grand' Mere, Quebec, in 1929 and the St. Johns Bridge across the Willamette River at Portland, Oregon, completed in 1931—both of these bridges having been designed by Robinson and Steinman of New York. Advocates of the "twisted-strand" system, as against the individual parallel wire cables, claim lower cost and shorter erection time.

The Grand' Mere Bridge, which we have just mentioned as one built by this method, has a main span of 950 feet and is the longest span suspension bridge in Canada. However, its chief point of interest is in the most unusual methods resorted to by its erectors. As it is located where rigorous winters have to be faced, the ingenious bridge builders turned this apparent disadvantage to their own good account. Not in the least dismayed when the river froze over solidly, they continued operations right on through the winter, using the ice for their working platform! Cables were strung on the frozen surface and lifted into place; huge sleds bearing seven- to ten-ton sections of the steel roadway trusses were hauled by teams of horses over the two-and-a-half-foot thick ice and lifted directly into place on the bridge. The schedule was planned so that the towers were under construction while the river was still freezing and before spring the entire suspension system with its rope cables, suspenders and roadway trusses had been assembled in place.

The St. Johns Bridge is interesting for several reasons. To start with, its 1,207-foot span places it in the rather exclusive list of bridges that exceed the 1,000-foot mark. Then it is the longest bridge yet built to be carried by twisted-strand cables and, until completion of the Golden Gate Bridge and the San Francisco-Oakland Bay Bridge, it was the longest bridge in the West. In designing its towers, the engineers adopted lines suggestive of Gothic architecture with the object of eliminating the none-too-sightly appearance that often results from use of conventional X-bracing in structures of this type. This bridge has a clearance of 205 feet over the water and carries a forty-foot roadway which forms an important connecting link in the state highway system.

Triborough Bridge Project.

Within the City of New York there has been opened a large bridge project the planning of which began back in 1916. This is the "Triborough Bridge," which is really not one bridge but a whole series of them, including several large spans and a total length of nearly three and a half miles of bridges and viaducts, without counting improvements in existing roadways, which were necessary in order to provide connections. Construction started in 1929 but was delayed by financial causes arising out of the depression and hence the bridge was not opened until 1936. This project was carried out under the direction of the Triborough Bridge Authority, a body created by action of the State Legislature and controlled by the city because power of appointment of its three commissioners was vested in the mayor. The bridge was financed by the Triborough Bridge Authority with the aid of a loan obtained from the Federal Emergency Administration of Public Works. Unlike the other bridges controlled by the City of New York, tolls are charged but after the bond issues have been amortized these may be ended.

As its title implies, this bridge project connects three boroughs, Queens, Manhattan and the Bronx, and on its route it crosses Wards and Randalls islands. Its longest span is of the suspension type, crossing the Hell Gate portion of the East River just south of the Hell Gate railroad arch. The new bridge there is carried by two cables, its main span being 1,380 feet with two side spans of 672 feet each, and clearance above the river at the middle of the span will be 135 feet to correspond with that of other East River bridges. The roadway provides for eight lanes of vehicles.

Three other bridges of importance are also included in the project, one being a single 350-foot span crossing the Bronx Kills that separate Randalls Island from the Bronx. This structure is designed to be convertible, in future, to a lift span. A plate girder bridge crosses Little Hell Gate separating the two islands, while crossing the Harlem River is a fourth bridge which is the vertical lift type and which we shall describe later in the chapter, Bridges That Move. In general arrangement the whole project forms a gigantic "T," since the approach from Harlem meets the Queens-Bronx roadway on the structure crossing Randalls Island. The bridge cost was about $44,200,000, and its completion gives, for the first time, a direct vehicular connection between Long Island and the mainland.

Twin Suspension Bridges over San Francisco Bay.

In our opening pages we gave a story of the great San Francisco-Oakland Bay Bridge and mentioned some difficulties encountered by its builders. We also pointed out how, from several points of view—amount of steel, cost, over-all length—this project is the biggest bridge in the world. Although forming only part of this record-breaking enterprise, the West Bay crossing extending from San Francisco to Yerba Buena Island (or "Goat Island," as it is perhaps better known) has its own distinct claims to fame. The main portion consists of two complete suspension bridges which are placed end to end and linked to a common anchorage in the center

119

of the channel. Each of these bridges has a main span of 2,310 feet and each has two end spans of 1,160 feet, figures exceeded only by the George Washington and Golden Gate bridges. The arrangement, in itself, establishes a new precedent, since this is the first time that two suspension bridges have been built end to end, with a common anchorage in midwater. To provide this mid-channel anchorage block, it was necessary to construct a great shell of concrete with its base resting upon bed-rock about 210 feet below water and its superstructure extending another 295 feet above. The entire height from base to top is thus about 504 feet and the immensity of this block can be pictured by considering it as equal to a forty-story building with a base of 197 by 92 feet. The total length of the West Bay section of the bridge is 10,450 feet as compared with a total length of 8,990 feet for the Golden Gate Bridge and 5,600 feet for the George Washington Bridge. Each being taken upon bases which are as nearly as possible comparable, these figures include both the suspended structure and the continuous truss spans from the San Francisco anchorage, in the case of the Bay Bridge.

Like the other bridges and the tunnel involved in the complete project, the West Bay crossing is double-decked. Its upper deck has a fifty-eight-foot roadway for six lanes of passenger cars while the lower deck carries a thirty-one-foot roadway for three lanes of commercial traffic and to one side of this roadway are two tracks for rapid transit trains. Clearance above the water under the middle of each main span is 200 feet, while at the center anchorage it is sixteen feet more.

To provide the connection between this West Bay crossing and the East Bay section (already described under "Modern Truss Bridges") about 540 feet of tunnel was bored through the crest of Goat Island. This is, as we have said, the largest bore tunnel in the world. Its height of fifty-two feet and width of sixty-six feet make its area greater than that of the Rove Barge Canal tunnel in France, formerly the largest tunnel. The tolls charged for use of the Bay Bridge, to be decreased gradually, are planned to cover maintenance costs with sufficient margin to amortize the construction expenditure in about twenty years, after which time the bridge is to be free.

Golden Gate Bridge, Longest Span in the World.

The Golden Gate Bridge at San Francisco, introduced in our opening pages, has a main span of 4,200 feet. This is by a substantial margin the longest span ever constructed, exceeding by 700 feet that of its nearest competitor, the George Washington Bridge. Like the latter bridge, it is of the suspension type. Its two end spans measure 1,125 feet each, so that the total length of the suspended structure is thus 6,450 feet, as compared with the 4,760 feet of the George Washington Bridge. Including the lesser spans forming part of its approaches, the over-all length of the Golden Gate Bridge is 8,990 feet. Its great towers reach the unprec-

121

edented height of 746 feet, equal of that of a sixty- to sixty-five story building, and they rest upon piers sunk down to solid rock a hundred feet below water. To eliminate the possibility of damage to the bridge resulting from an earthquake, the foundations have been sunk twenty-five feet into the rock.

The total width of the bridge floor is eighty-one feet, including a sixty-foot roadway and two ten-and-a-half-foot sidewalks, no provision being made for railway traffic. Two cables, each containing 27,572 individual wires, carry this structure at a height which leaves 220 feet clearance over the water at the middle of the span. After compacting, these cables measure thirty-six and one-half inches. This is half an inch more than each of the four cables of the George Washington Bridge, which were formerly the largest bridge cables in use. So much steel was required to construct the Golden Gate Bridge towers that it alone exceeded the entire amount used in constructing the great Quebec Bridge which, until 1928, was the longest span ever built and which is still the longest existing span of the cantilever type. About 900 freight cars were required to carry this steel to the site of the bridge.

In addition to having the longest span, the Golden Gate Bridge also has several other features of distinction. Its San Francisco pier was the first bridge pier ever built in deep open water and the bridge itself is the only structure ever built across the outer mouth of an important ocean harbor. In consequence of this, one of its towers is being made a station of the United States Lighthouse Service and will carry a beacon for the guidance of ships at sea. The entire cost of the bridge, exclusive of the north and south approach roads (forming a part of the state highway system), will be defrayed out of a $35,000,000 bond issue. Tolls charged are expected to amortize this cost in about forty years.

Chapter X

Reinforced-concrete Bridges

MOST concrete bridges are of recent construction and because of this there is a common tendency to think of concrete as a modern development. Yet this is far from the truth, for concrete itself dates back to the Romans and it is only the use of steel-reinforced concrete that is new. The ancient bridges were built by using such an excess of material so tremendous that any danger of collapse was removed. Today concrete structures are scientifically designed and reinforced with steel bars, the steel being used to resist tensile loads while the concrete carries the compressive stresses.

It takes no more than a glance at one of our modern open-frame concrete bridges to show the extent to which this refinement has been carried. No longer do we see the tremendous mass of material that was formerly used above the arch; instead, we find slender vertical pillars running from the arch up to support the roadway. This is what engineers call "open-spandrel" construction because the spandrels, or spaces between the arches and the roadway, are left open. Sometimes the sides are faced with ornamental stone or have curtain walls of concrete, giving to the eye the appearance of a solid

124

mass, although it is actually an open structure. Because of the economy of material, the open-spandrel type of design is becoming general where concrete is selected for the construction of large bridges. For smaller bridges an arch with retaining-wall sides is often used, the space above the arch and between these sides being filled with earth to carry the roadway. This filling of earth naturally adds more dead load to an arch, so it is done only where the cost of forms for open spandrels is not justified by the material savings that would result from their use.

All of these remarks, of course, apply only to arch bridges and, while this represents the typical concrete bridge, others have been built. It is quite a simple matter to design truss bridges of reinforced concrete and some have been constructed, a concrete cantilever structure being described in our chapter, More Unusual Bridges.

With the introduction of steel reinforcing, concrete became a material of increased value to bridge builders, therefore many recent bridges are of this type of construction. One of the greatest concrete bridges ever built was put into use in November of 1915 when trains began operating over the Lackawanna Railroad's majestic Tunkhannock Viaduct, which has made world-famous the little creek after which it was named. This gigantic structure of reinforced concrete, bridging across a great valley and dwarfing the little creek below, is a modern version of the great bridges that were built to supply ancient Rome with its water. But the Roman structures were puny beside this modern erection with its 162,000 cubic yards of concrete, its twelve arches and its double-track roadbed, 240 feet above the creek level. Of the arches ten 180-foot spans are visible to the eye. Unseen, since they are covered by fill, are two additional arches of one-hundred-foot span, one at each end.

The total length of the viaduct is 2,375 feet and it forms part of the Nicholson Cutoff which was built to eliminate bad grades, curves totaling six-and-three-quarter complete turns, and some three and a half miles of distance, from the railroad's main line between Scranton, Pennsylvania, and Elmira, New York. In spite of all efforts to economize in the use of materials, the grand scale of this project made it necessary to use about 162,000 cubic yards of concrete and some 2,275,000 pounds of reinforcing steel in its construction. Concrete was selected by the railroad engineers only after investigating both this material and steel, their decision favoring the concrete because of lower maintenance and despite somewhat higher first cost.

Two Recent Concrete Bridges.

The George Westinghouse Bridge was erected as part of the Lincoln Highway where it passes through the City of Pittsburgh. This bridge crosses the Pennsylvania Railroad yards and a small creek, at a height of 200 feet above the creek level. It consists of five arches, the central one with its span of 460 feet being the longest reinforced concrete arch in America, while two side spans are each 295 feet. Construction began in May of 1930 and the bridge was completed in December of 1931. The new Vermillion River Bridge at Danville, Illinois, is another excellent example of our modern type of concrete bridges and both bridges illustrate the extent to which engineers have eliminated surplus material. Indeed, the slender proportions of each of these bridges make it hard to realize that they are not really steel structures which have been merely encased in concrete.

About fifty miles up the Dnieper River from the famous Dnieprostroy electric power-plant development in Russia, there is a reinforced-concrete bridge of recent construction which has a rather unusual history. A bridge at this site was planned during the old Czarist regime in Russia and construction began during the early years of the World War. The tremendous economic upheaval which followed the revolution interrupted its construction and work was abandoned for many years.

However, in 1931 the Soviet engineers, in association with an American consultant, designed a new structure, which was recently completed. This is a railroad bridge of the open-spandrel type of reinforced-concrete arch and it has fourteen 170-foot arches in addition to three lesser ones, several steel trusses and some girder spans. The entire bridge is 5,350 feet long, of which a distance of about 4,600 feet is constructed of concrete. This bridge was built in 1931–1932, being completed in the latter year after sixteen months of work. To permit

127

completion of concreting before winter set in, it was
necessary to build enough falsework trusses to provide
for each of the concrete spans. All arches were then
poured simultaneously, most of the concrete being mixed
on the shore and carried out to the arches by means of a
cableway. Since the piers had been constructed during
the early days of the project, this bridge has the distinction of having been started by the Czarist government
and completed about a decade and a half later by the
Soviets, the Soviet-built structure standing upon the
Czarist-built piers.

There were bridges of artistic merit in Europe as
early as the Roman period and many beautiful European bridges have been in existence for several centuries.
It is only within the last one hundred years, however,
that much consideration has been given to the incorporation of artistic beauty in bridges in the United
States. During the earlier history of our country, bridge
builders had little time for spending much thought on
that feature of the work. With the development of parks
and parkways in the United States, there is far more
consideration given here to this angle of bridge building
in our own time. Hence we find many recent bridges of
beautiful proportions, the preference apparently being
given to stone and concrete when the structure is to become a unit in some parkway system. Such bridges are
now designed by engineers and architects working together and in close cooperation with landscape architects. Today, practically every large city can show

FIG. 36.—Building the Tunkhannock Creek Viaduct.

FIG. 37.—Grandfey Viaduct of the Swiss Federal Railroads, at Fribourg.

FIG. 38.—Mill Road Bridge, Hutchinson River Parkway, Westchester County, New York.

FIG. 39.—One of the Long Island State Parkway bridges.

FIG. 40.—Harway Avenue twin bascule bridges, Coney Island, New York.

FIG. 41.—Buzzards Bay Bridge over Cape Cod Canal has the longest lift span in the world.

FIG. 42.—Completing the Triborough Bridge lift span over the Harlem River.

bridges of the "parkway" type and some recently developed parkways make liberal use of artistic bridges in the elimination of grade crossings. In some of these parkways the engineers have eliminated nearly all grade crossings, intersecting roadways being carried over or under their new parkway by use of numerous stone or stone-faced-concrete bridges.

In some recent cases, parkway bridges have been constructed upon a structural steel frame built into the abutments at each side and extending through the arch to carry its load after the manner of a cantilever structure. This steel frame is often encased in concrete and faced with stone to give the appearance of a very graceful light stone arch. Parkway bridges are characterized by their relatively short span, only sufficient to cross a main highway, and by the special consideration which is given to their appearance.

Chapter XI

Bridges That Move

The Earliest Lift Bridges.

BRIDGES of the type that lift evidently came into use in the days when gallant knights rescued beautiful maidens from fiery dragons and bore them triumphantly home to their medieval castles, for about the earliest kind was the lifting drawbridge that was used to cross the moat surrounding an old castle. This was merely a wooden platform hinged at its inner end while its outer end was linked to chains which were used to raise it up when passage into the castle was to be closed against enemies. Movable wooden bridges were used also for the defense of cities as far back as the Roman days, the plank floor or a short section of the bridge being removed to interrupt anyone's crossing. As men began to build bridges over canals and rivers, their interference with free passage of water craft soon made the movable bridge a necessity. Many of the early movable bridges were undoubtedly of wood, but since they were relatively short-lived, we have to base our assumption more upon abstract reasoning than upon concrete evidence. In other cases, and these we know to be founded on fact, floating

130

bridges were built upon boats or pontoons with sections which could be floated to one side. Later, a variety of radically different kinds of movable bridges came into use, including among them the swing type, rolling lift bridges and vertical lift bridges, the name of each aptly describing its principle of operation. The bascule type, which is in very general use today, is a modern version of the old castle drawbridge, but in place of the crude lifting chains it has a motor-operated mechanism and it is built of steel instead of wood.

London's Tower Bridge.

One of the best known of our older, but still existing, movable bridges is the Tower Bridge over the Thames at London, the construction of which began in 1886 and took until 1894. This bridge has a central span of 200 feet which consists of two bascules that meet in the middle. At the time of its erection, the bridge was regarded as a remarkable piece of engineering. At each end of the central span, connecting with the shores, is a suspension span carried by an unusual arrangement of suspension linking which was adopted for the purpose of stiffening the structure. The roadway is thirty-two feet wide, with sidewalks on each side which bring the total width up to forty-nine feet.

Two steel towers which support the structure are so completely encased in masonry that few visitors to the city realize that they are not wholly of stone. These are placed well out in the river to support the lifting bascules and the suspension spans link them with the shores. The towers are designed to resemble the towers of an old castle, doubtless because of their proximity to the Tower of London, from which the bridge takes its name. Extending 206 feet above the roadway they form a distinctive feature of the bridge and leave a marked impression in the recollection of visitors to the city.

Above the lifting span is a smaller footbridge, running between the two towers and near their tops. This is reached by means of elevators and is intended for the use of pedestrians when the highway bridge is open. The lifting bascules are counterweighted at their inner ends with nearly a million pounds of ballast to balance the span portions and thus relieve the machinery of unnecessary load. Operation is by hydraulic power, two 360-horsepower pumps being used to supply the necessary pressure to a storage tank. The opening and closing of the bridge are controlled from cabins on the piers.

No visitor to the city of Chicago has failed to observe the unusual number of lifting-type bridges which that city found necessary to build over the Chicago River for the passage of vehicles and foot passengers. These bascule-type bridges have numerous advantages for carrying street traffic over rivers where a movable bridge is necessary and where appearance must be considered. It would take considerable imagination to class as "good-looking" the average swing or lift bridge of the truss type, but the bascule construction adapts itself well to artistic treatment and adaptation to surroundings.

132

Hence there is nothing surprising in the information that Chicago's North Wabash Avenue Bridge, one of her recent bascules, was designed "The most beautiful steel bridge built in 1930" and thus decorated with a bronze tablet commemorating the occasion. This bridge is of the double-lift, pivoted type with a span of 269 feet as measured from center to center of the trunnions, or pivots. It has a sixty-foot roadway with two fifteen-foot sidewalks. As customary, this bridge is operated by motor drives which rapidly lift the leaves, with their total weight of over five million pounds, up to a steep angle thus leaving the river passage absolutely clear of obstruction at any height.

Another particularly beautiful bascule is included as part of the Arlington Memorial Bridge crossing the Potomac River at Washington, D.C. This is a double bascule, forming one of the spans in what is otherwise an arch bridge of concrete construction faced with white granite. Thus, the opening span is flanked on each end by stone arches. Since architectural treatment was an important consideration in the whole bridge, a bascule-lift span was selected as best suited to carry out the architectural appearance of the adjacent arches. The structural steel underframe of each leaf of the bascule is faced with ornamental steelwork, following the general contour of the flanking arches, while its side railings are similarly matched. When the bascule draws are closed, it is surprising to see how well these blend with the rest of the bridge. Only a most observant person

133

would notice that one of the spans is of the movable type. This lifting span is one of the largest and heaviest of its kind in the world. Each of the two leaves measures 108 feet, hence the total opening is 216 feet. The eight arches forming the rest of the bridge range from 166 to 180 feet in span and the total length of the whole bridge is 2,143 feet. Its roadway is sixty feet wide and there are two fourteen-foot sidewalks. Because of the unusual weight of the lift span, about 2,400 tons for each leaf, a whole ship cargo of iron ore was mixed with the concrete forming the counterweights in order to make these sufficiently heavy without too much bulk. The bridge was designed by Joseph B. Strauss, who has been responsible for many bascule spans throughout the country and who directed the design and construction of the Golden Gate Bridge at San Francisco.

Spanning the Suisun Bay near Martinez, California, is a 5,600-foot double-track bridge of the Southern Pacific Railway consisting of seven 526-foot main spans of modified Warren truss type, two lesser spans of parallel-chord Warren truss, several plate-girder spans and a 328-foot vertical lift span which is also of the Warren truss type. This lifting span is representative of modern practice in that kind of bridge, having been constructed in 1929–1930. Upon each of its two towers are great sheaves, or pulleys, over which pass heavy steel-wire ropes carrying the great counterweights that serve to counterbalance the movable portion. The lifting span is raised by means of electric motors and, in the upper position, leaves sufficient clearance to permit the passage of ocean vessels.

For a time the longest of all lifting bridges, and still the longest highway lift bridge in the world, is the 534-foot movable span of the Burlington-Bristol highway bridge which crosses the Delaware River south of Trenton, New Jersey. This is a rather unusual bridge, not only for exceptional length in the movable class but also because the top chord members of the side-span trusses have been designed to match the curves of the lifting-span trusses. Thus, when the bridge is lowered, the main and end spans have the appearance of being one continuous truss from end to end. Sixteen two-inch steel wire ropes are used to carry the two concrete counterweights (each weighing 620 tons) which are required to counterbalance the 1,240-ton weight of the lifting span. The bridge is operated by means of two eighty-horsepower electric motors, which seem remarkably small for lifting so much weight seventy-four feet upwards in about two minutes! These motors operate the bridge by means of two one-and-three-eighths-inch steel-wire ropes fastened at each of its four corners. The ropes are secured to the top and the bottom of the towers, passing over drums connected with the electric motors and mounted on the movable section. By means of the ropes, the bridge is hauled up or hauled down, the counterweights being designed to approximately balance its weight so that a minimum of power and time is required for operation.

Longest Lift Span in the World.

To the Buzzards Bay Bridge, completed in 1935 to carry the New York, New Haven and Hartford Railroad tracks over the western end of the Cape Cod Canal, belongs the distinction of having the longest lifting span in the world. This bridge is of the vertically-moving type, its lifting section of 544 feet exceeding that of the Burlington-Bristol bridge by ten feet. It also rises to unusual height, leaving a clear headroom of 139 feet over the water when the span is up.

The bridge was erected as an essential part of the canal improvement work, the widening of this waterway necessitating the removal of the older 160-foot-span bascule which the new structure replaces. Being placed at the entrance to the canal, the structure became more or less of a "gateway," with its imposing size and its clear passage of 500 feet between piers. Hence, particular attention had to be given to the appearance, for the two tall towers housing the mechanism and serving as guides for the movable portion would stand out prominently as the canal was approached from the water. These towers were, therefore, treated as pylons, or shafts, marking this entrance and they have been surmounted by tops which tend to carry out the effect. Within the rooms forming those tops, the operating mechanism is located, so they serve a practical as well as an ornamental purpose. The sixty-nine-foot-deep trusses forming the structure are spaced twenty-seven feet apart and between them is carried the single track of the railroad.

Instead of the bronze bearings so generally used, the cable sheaves were provided with roller bearings for the purpose of economy in operation. The designing engineers estimated that adoption of these roller bearings would cut the required motor horsepower from 600 to 300, due solely to lowered friction.

Lift Span for the Triborough Bridge Project.

Under the head of "Modern Suspension Bridges," we gave a general description of the Triborough Bridge project and made reference to the Harlem River lift bridge which is included in the construction. On account of conditions affecting approach on the Bronx side, the Harlem River has to be crossed at a considerably lower level than is maintained for the East River crossing of the same project. It thus became necessary to provide a movable bridge, so that the river channel would not become restricted to smaller vessels. This is a lift bridge of rather unusual design and distinctly artistic appearance. The movable span is 310 feet long and carries two thirty-and-a-half-foot roadways; in the normal position it leaves a clearance of fifty-five feet at mean high-water level, or enough to permit the passage of many fairly large vessels. When the span is raised, this clearance is increased to 135 feet, thus equaling the clearance of other East River bridges. At each end is a side span, one being just under 242 feet, the other just under 153 feet, with their top chords arranged to correspond to the height of the center and lift truss. The lift span and its two side spans thus present the appearance of a continuous structure when the bridge is down. This is practically the only concession that was made exclusively for the sake of appearance, since the rest of this bridge follows our modern trend towards frank combination of structure with pleasing lines, without resorting to masonry for concealment.

Chapter XII

Some Unusual Bridges

Where Ships Pass over Street Cars.

WINDING its way through the industrial area of southern
Scotland is an old canal, opened in 1792, which still remains an important artery for the transport of freight,
in spite of the extensive railroad construction which began some twenty years later. This generally prosaic and
rather uninteresting waterway is the thirty-five-mile
Forth and Clyde Canal, connecting the Firth of Forth
on the east coast with the River Clyde on the west.

To most people of Glasgow, the part that passes
through their city is just a "dirty old canal." But to the
more observant this historic old waterway has a few
interesting features and one is found in the spot where
it was necessary to bridge the canal over an important
city street. Heading northwest towards the Maryhill district, while comfortably seated on the upper deck of one
of Glasgow's excellent street cars, a casual passenger
seldom notices anything unusual as the car speeds under
an old stone bridge, the damp arch of which reveberates
with the sing of the overhead trolley. It is only upon
some infrequent occasion that he happens to look up in
time to see a strange vision as the car nears the bridge.
For, from his position below he may glimpse, moving

139

along on what seems to be dry land above, the masts of a small freighter slowly wending its way towards the nearby locks that will start it on its way down to sea level! And at Temple Bridge, a short distance away, we find another unusual case of bridging, for here is a roadway crossing over the canal while at the same point a railroad passes at an angle beneath the waterway—each of the highways of three kinds of transportation upon a different level.

Bridging the Great Salt Lake.

Construction of the first bridge to exceed the length of Caligula's historic bridge of boats came about only when the Southern Pacific built its famous Lucin-Ogden Cutoff, a stretch of track that runs across the Great Salt Lake between Ogden and Lucin, Utah. Work began in 1902, the purpose being to reduce the route distance by some forty-three miles, as well as to eliminate some undesirable grades. Part of the cutoff is in the form of an embankment or fill built out into the Lake, but the center part, of some twenty miles, is a wood-pile trestle which, even to this day, remains the longest stretch of trestle bridge ever built. Surveys showed the maximum depth of the lake to be thirty feet and for most of the distance it was much less.

On the face of it, the job looked comparatively simple and so the work was started, beginning at each side and working out to meet near the center. Fill was carried out from each shore and, as deeper water was reached, prep-

140

arations were made to begin pile driving. The pile driver was set up and the first pile lifted into place for driving. Down came the big hammer and, to the surprise of all, the twenty-six-foot-long pile went right out of sight at the first blow! Rather taken aback at the unexpected softness of the bed, the construction gang took another pile, this one about twenty-eight feet long, and set it directly on top of the first. Again the hammer fell and again the amazed crew found itself looking at the surface of the water into which the second pile had completely disappeared! Investigation showed that they had chosen a part of the lake bed where the salt-encrusted bottom was underlaid with mud fully fifty feet deep. The problem was finally solved by driving seventy-foot piles and filling the softer spots of the bed with dirt to aid in furnishing support.

Work was pushed steadily and by March of 1903 rails were laid out on the completed portion of the embankments. The pile-driving trouble, however, was not to be the end of difficulties, for the first construction locomotive to run out on the section of track pitched into the lake when the treacherous salt-crust bottom suddenly gave way under the added weight and the whole embankment sank badly. This was remedied by adding more fill. Again the work went on and it was beginning to look as if the troubles were over when, on April 2, 1903, a part of the trestle work sank beneath the weight of a construction train and the entire train was pitched into the lake.

141

By this time the Southern Pacific was beginning to realize that it had a job on its hands. Even the staid old *Engineering News,* chronicling the progress of the work from time to time, was beginning to refer to the whole project as a "failure." Having gone this far, the railroad was determined to carry the work through. More men were added until, by July of 1903, the construction forces reached the enormous figure of about 3,000 men. Trainload after trainload of fill was deposited in the soft mud bed and gradually the sinking troubles came to an end. The cutoff was opened on November 26, 1903, the total cost having reached $4,200,000 before the roadbed was considered sufficiently sound to permit the operation of passenger trains. With the Lucin Cutoff in operation, a bridge-length record that had stood for almost nineteen centuries passed from the ghostly hands of Caius Caesar Caligula into the custody of the very real Southern Pacific Railroad.

Where the Railroad Went Out to Sea.

Not to be outdone by this bridging of a lake, another railroad began a still more daring construction venture just a few years later. This resulted in the Key West Extension, built at a cost of about $49,000,000. It was a conception of the late Henry M. Flagler and under his management it was completed in the year before his death.

Weaving its way along a semitropical coast through the magic city of Miami, the Florida East Coast Railway continued south to Homestead, the business center of an agricultural area at the tip of the Florida peninsula. One might well have expected the line to terminate here, for ahead there is nothing but sea. Instead, it continued south, heading right out over the open sea upon one of the most audacious engineering accomplishments that was ever attempted. Its like has never since been duplicated. Passengers to Key West moving over these miles of bridgework and fill connecting little islands used to experience the unique sensation of crossing the ocean in a railroad train. For at some points in their 110-mile trip it took indeed a keen eye to detect the tiny speck of land that showed itself upon a distant horizon.

This remarkable piece of railroad construction was begun in the fall of 1905 and was put into service in 1912, temporary service to Knights Key being operated a short time before completion of the remaining twenty-five miles of line to Key West. The route covered about 110 miles of virtually open sea, jumping from island to island along the southwest course of the string of Florida Keys. About thirty miles actually did lie over open water, twenty-four miles of this being constructed by building an embankment in the shallow water. The other six miles consisted of bridges, some being as much as two miles in length. Only the comparatively shallow water made the project possible, the depth seldom exceeding ten feet although in some cases it reached sixteen and twenty feet.

When this project was first contemplated, it was

143

found impossible to get any contractor who would bid on its construction. The obstacles were so many and the work so unusual that no one would take the risk of constructing the line at a fixed price. Eventually, the railroad itself undertook the work, organizing a construction department that at times employed as many as 5,000 or 6,000 men. The chief engineer practically lived on a launch and so much of the work was in open water that it took a fleet of eight shallow-draft river steamers and many small launches to transport men and materials along the route. Even the water used for mixing concrete had to be taken by boat from Miami, for salt water cannot be used successfully in concrete construction. The tremendous working force was organized and directed like an army in action, fifteen camps being in operation at once during part of the six-year construction period.

The difficulties that were encountered may well be imagined. In some stretches it became necessary to construct temporary supports on piles to provide a platform for surveyors; there was no other way of fixing a point for measurement in the sea! Most of the work was constructed upon a soft coral rock, into which it was necessary to drive piles to support the piers and arches. Those portions which are exposed to the open sea were built of reinforced concrete in order to resist damage by waves in stormy weather. The thoroughness with which this construction was carried out is evidenced by the several severe tropical storms that it withstood for twenty-three years after its completion. Trees had been

43.—Twenty miles of trestle carry the Southern Pacific tracks over Great Salt Lake.

Fig. 44.—Key West Extension, when the railroad went out to sea.

FIG. 45.—Four and three-quarter miles of trestle support Lake Pontchartrain Bridg

FIG. 46.—Mahi Bridge of the Bombay, Baroda and Central India Railway is designe
withstand complete submersion during floods.

FIG. 47.—Bastei Bridge, built in 1851 to connect mountain peaks near Dresden. (*Photograph by Alfred Glöckner.*)

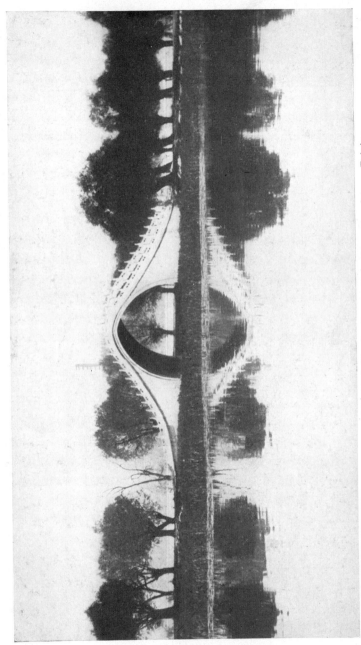

FIG. 48.—"Camel back" bridge in the summer palace grounds near Peiping.

uprooted, houses destroyed and wires brought down, but the Key West Extension viaducts remained until service was finally interrupted by an exceptionally violent hurricane in the fall of 1935.

The concrete viaduct running from Long Key to Conch Key is about two miles long and has almost 200 arches resting on piles in water that is sixteen feet deep at points. All of this part of the construction had to be carried out by use of boats and floating equipment. Flagler, who was in his seventy-sixth year when the work began, lived just long enough to see his dream realized, for his end came in 1913, the year after the extension was opened. When the line was running, the tourist or business man headed for Havana passed over this remarkable structure, gazing out of the dining-car windows to watch the waves dash impotently against the staunch concrete structure over which he was traveling. But the use of the extension was not confined to passengers, for almost daily long trains of freight cars, transferred by boat from Cuba to Key West, could have been seen rolling their way to the mainland.

Unfortunately, this experience is no longer possible, for train service was discontinued after the hurricane of 1935, the cost of repairs causing the depression-hit railroad to abandon service. However, the extension may go back into service in a new guise, for the Monroe County Commissioners plan its conversion into a motor highway and the State of Florida may soon boast of a "highway that runs out to sea."

145

Chapter XIII
More Unusual Bridges

Lindenthal's North River Bridge Project.

THIS book was undertaken with the intention of confining it to bridges which had actually been built or were still under construction. Although that was the original plan, the grand scale of Lindenthal's projected Hudson River Bridge warrants some description—particularly in view of the high reputation of the designer.

Gustav Lindenthal was responsible for the design of many American bridges, of which we have mentioned only a few in these pages. He showed interest in Hudson River bridge proposals as far back as 1887 and his designs since that time have included several bridges at different locations. The last of these was planned for the vicinity of 57th Street, New York City, and for sheer immensity this proposed structure dwarfs even the largest bridges which we have built to date. While other, subsequent, Hudson River crossing facilities make it highly improbable that Lindenthal's bridge will ever be constructed, its gigantic size makes a description of some interest. His 1923 design called for a 3,240-foot eyebar chain suspension bridge span over the river. So

146

far as span alone is concerned, this has since been exceeded by the 3,500-foot George Washington Bridge and the 4,200-foot Golden Gate Bridge. However, the tremendous size of his project has never been approached by any other bridges to date. For Lindenthal's structure was planned to carry *twelve* rapid transit railroad tracks on a lower deck while its upper deck would carry two trolley car tracks, two bus lanes, two fifteen-foot sidewalks and no less than *sixteen* lanes of trucks and passenger vehicles.

The total width of the bridge floor was to be 235 feet, as against 160 feet for the Sydney Harbour Bridge, the widest built to date. Its cost with approaches was estimated at $180,000,000, as against the $77,000,000 cost of the San Francisco Bay Bridge, the most ambitious bridge project to this time. The enormous cost of the projected "North River Bridge" became an insurmountable barrier to its realization and, in the meantime, construction of other facilities greatly restricted the need for such a bridge. In addition, other engineers have questioned the advisability of concentrating such tremendous capacity in one bridge, preferring the plan of dividing it over two or more bridges or tunnels to eliminate the danger of excessive traffic congestion. But, although Lindenthal's North River Bridge is unlikely ever to become a tangible reality, his plans warrant a place in any record of bridge history.

Running four and three-quarter miles across Lake Pontchartrain, over water averaging about ten feet in

147

depth, is a concrete bridge of the trestle type which was the longest modern highway bridge built prior to the San Francisco Bay Bridge. Construction began in October of 1926 and this unusual bridge was opened in the following year, 2,796 precast concrete piles having been driven into the lake bed to provide the support. The bridge consists of about 700 spans of thirty-five feet each in addition to two bascule-type drawbridges of steel truss construction and its roadway is about fifteen feet above the water.

One of the chief problems in building this bridge was that of transporting material to the site, since the adjacent ground at each end was low and wet. This made it necessary to place the pile-casting and construction plant about twelve miles away, the precast piles and other materials being transported to the site on barges. No less than thirty-six barges and eleven towboats were required for carrying these materials, while three large floating pile drivers were used to drive the eighty-foot-long and two-foot-square concrete piles. Water for concrete used in constructing the bridge roadway was obtained by sinking wells into the lake bottom along the course. While the piles were driven, floating mixing plants followed—moving along from point to point as the thirty-foot-wide roadway slabs were poured. The project is operated as a toll bridge and in addition to eliminating two ferry crossings it saves about nine miles as compared with the former route.

148

The Sky Ride.

An amusement device taking the form of a transporter type of suspension bridge was erected in connection with Chicago's Century of Progress Exposition in 1933–1934. This was the "Sky Ride," a device consisting of two 628-foot steel towers surmounted by observation platforms and carrying (at a height of about 200 feet) a suspension system upon which cars transported passengers across the 1,850-foot space between. Sightseers were lifted to the transportation level and observation platforms by means of elevators, of which there were four in each tower. The observation platforms were designed to accommodate as many as 300 persons at a height exceeding that of Chicago's highest skyscraper. From these platforms the visitor could see four states, in addition to being afforded an excellent bird's eye view of the exposition itself. The Sky-Ride suspension system was rather unique, for its stiffening was provided by the suspension system instead of by trusses on the track level. The stiffening system was thus formed entirely of steel-wire rope! In place of ordinary rails were two wire-rope tracks, each consisting of a pair of wire ropes pulled taut under sufficient tension to eliminate noticeable sag and supported at frequent intervals by the suspension system. Still another novel feature was the use of pivoted counterweights instead of the usual immovable mass anchorages for securing the suspension cable ends. This last feature had the advantage of giving a predetermined load in the cable system, thus eliminat-

149

ing sag changes otherwise caused by temperature variations. In the fabrication of the towers, welding was used
instead of shop rivets. This work involved about nineteen miles of automatic fillet weld, using three and a
half tons of weld metal and making the largest structural welding job to date.

Double-decked passenger cars providing seats for
thirty-six persons traveled along the steel ropes running
from tower to tower. Arriving at a tower, they circled
around it, paused to unload and load, and then returned
to their starting point. More than four million passengers were carried without a single accident. Although
erected as an amusement device, the Sky Ride created
considerable interest among engineers because of the
several unusual features involved in its design and construction. Its conception originated with a Scotchman
by the name of W. C. Hamilton, who had erected and
successfully operated a somewhat similar device in
Great Britain. The structure was designed by Robinson
and Steinman, its construction being financed by several large concerns participating in its erection and
equipment.

Conowingo—a Dam That Is also a Bridge.

Sometimes we find a structure which, as a by-product
of its main function, also serves as a bridge. One of these
is the Conowingo Dam, located on the Susquehanna
River in Cecil County, Maryland, near the site of the
former town of Conowingo. This once was a quaint little

town on Baltimore Pike, the main highway from Philadelphia to Baltimore. In the course of developing sources of electric power to supply Philadelphia and other cities in that industrial region, the Philadelphia Electric Company undertook the conversion of water power from the Susquehanna River. A dam was built at the site of the little town whose name it now perpetuates and a lake that covers some fourteen square miles was formed by blocking the normal flow of the river at this point. Under the new lake there disappeared all remaining traces of the town of Conowingo and, in its place, the engineers and builders left the great dam and the power plant with its present capacity of 378,000 horsepower. By the time that all future generators are installed, the plant will eventually reach 594,000 horsepower.

The lake formed by the construction of the dam cut off a section of the Baltimore Pike passing through the former town of Conowingo and, since this was an important highway, a substitute route had to be provided. So in place of the old route the builders constructed new roadways that lead right up to each side of the dam. Then, above the dam itself, they constructed a bridge that crosses directly over its great spillways, past its large power plant, and thence across the artificial lake. As he drives by the substantial buildings of the power plant, it is difficult for the passing motorist to realize that he is actually crossing a bridge; it seems so much more like firm ground. For motorists, the net result of

151

this power development was a slightly shorter route with better grades. While Conowingo is not the only dam to serve also as a bridge, it provides a sight not often repeated during trips around the country.

Where a Bridge Carries a Bridge.

Bridge builders often face problems that tax their ingenuity when railroads have to be carried through mountain ranges. This is particularly true where the mountains rise precipitously from each side of some narrow gully, leaving no room for workers to obtain a foothold without blasting every step out of solid rock, clinging to the sides or swinging from suspended platforms as they work. In October of 1928, the Paris, Lyons and Mediterranean Railway opened a new forty-mile link connecting with the Italian State Railways and providing a short cut between Marseilles and Turin. This new line leaves the old at Nice and joins the Italian road at San Dalmazza, near the border, the route crossing wild mountain country that required endless bridges, viaducts and tunnels. Among the numerous problems encountered, one was that faced by the engineers in bridging a narrow gorge of the Bevera River, where both sides rose almost perpendicularly. To make matters worse an acute-angle crossing had to be made, necessitating a most expensive bridge if it were built in one span, since the acute angle greatly increased the length required. Yet the narrowness of the stream eliminated any possibility of using a center pier to support two spans.

Finally the unique plan was devised of building a bridge to support the bridge.

At right angles to the railroad track and at some distance below it, an arch was built from wall to wall of the chasm. This arch was then used to serve the purpose of a center support for the main bridge above. The lower bridge is a masonry arch of eighty-two-foot span with a height of sixty-four feet above the water; the railroad bridge which it carries consists of two spans of 150-foot steel trusses. This gorge is so steep that approaches to the bridge are built almost flat against its sides. They look like parts of the rock itself, instead of what they really are—heavy masonry structures with footings extending up from near the bottom of the gorge.

At the old Scottish town of Montrose there was recently built a reinforced concrete bridge of the cantilever truss type. This novel structure was erected to replace the historic Montrose Suspension Bridge, which was about a hundred years old and had become inadequate to meet the requirements of modern traffic. The new bridge uses the old approaches and abutments originally constructed for the suspension bridge which it replaced, but new piers were built in the river to replace the original ones. The new concrete bridge has a central cantilever span of 216 feet and on each end is an anchor span of 150 feet. The main part of each truss is above the roadway and its top chord drops in a sweeping curve from the towers in a manner that resembles the curve of a suspension cable. But instead of the small proportions of chains or cables, they are of considerable size while a form of "Warren truss" ties them to lower members which approximately follow the roadway line. To carry the tensile stresses in these upper members there are cast in the concrete seventy-six steel bars, each one and a half inches in diameter. A few years after the Montrose bridge was built; another reinforced-concrete cantilever bridge was constructed at Vaux sur Yonne in France.

Some engineers have criticized concrete cantilever bridges as uneconomic because the concrete is used in tension members and this material is suitable only for compression. They have pointed out that since enough reinforcing steel must be added to take the entire tensile load, concrete serves no purpose in these parts. In refutation, the concrete cantilever builders claimed that the total cost of their bridge was lower, in spite of this condition. Although very few concrete cantilever truss bridges have been built to date, there are many reinforced concrete truss bridges of the "bowstring" form in Europe and a few have been built in this country. In this type of structure, reinforced concrete seems more logical, since the top chord is subjected to compression and the concrete can take this load satisfactorily.

The Highest Bridge in the World.

Several times throughout these pages we have mentioned the frequency with which bridge records have been made and broken, particularly within the past cen-

154

tury of rapid engineering development. But, in 1929, there was built in Colorado one bridge which is likely to retain its particular type of record for many years. This is the Royal Gorge Bridge spanning the Arkansas River, at the gorge after which it is named, with the remarkable height of 1,050 feet above the stream. Strange to say, no long and winding approach construction was necessary to reach this tremendous height, for the bridge floor was built on about the same level as the precipitous rocks that tower threateningly over the comparatively narrow gorge. Among engineers this bridge excited little interest. To them its modest eighteen-foot roadway and its 880-foot span make it a structure of secondary importance. Even the unusual feature of its having four suspension cable towers, instead of the customary two, was given merely casual mention in engineering magazines at the time of its construction. For it is only a freak of nature in creating a chasm of such enormous depth that gives to this bridge its unique distinction of being the highest bridge in the world.

are usually built of special steel piles having interlocking edges which form a practically watertight wall.

In the building of a cofferdam the piling is driven into place and some impervious material like clay is usually deposited in the river directly against the outside to make the enclosure more nearly watertight. The box is then braced internally with heavy timbers to withstand the great pressure which will result from the water on the outside, once the cofferdam has been emptied. The space enclosed by the cofferdam is then pumped free of water and within the space thus protected excavation of the river bed is carried on "in the dry." This expression has a slightly ironical tinge, since the work is far from being really dry. As one may well suppose, a certain amount of water leaks constantly into the cofferdam through the spaces between the piles and through the bottom, while the work is going on. It requires almost continual pumping to keep the bottom sufficiently clear of water to permit working but, excepting for this, the work does go on within the cofferdam in much the same way as it would above water level.

When excavations are complete, concrete footings are poured and upon these the pier is built until it is higher than water level. Once this stage is reached, water is allowed to flow back into the cofferdam, the piling is pulled out and any clay which may have been dumped outside of it can be removed. The pier is then ready for the construction of the superstructure.

This open cofferdam method of construction is much

160

FIG. 49.—Cofferdams for the New Jersey piers of the George Washington Bridge.

FIG. 50.—Installing the first eyebars, New York anchorage, George Washington Bridge.

FIG. 51.—Covered bridge over the Juniata River in Pennsylvania, built in 1818.

Fig. 52.—Mount Hope Bridge, longest span in New England. (*Photograph by AMEMYA.*)

older than the pneumatic caisson system, the latter being a fairly recent development which has come with the great advancement in engineering construction within the past hundred years. Because it permits work to be done in the open, cofferdam construction is nearly always lower in cost than caisson construction, but its practical depth limits are less than depths attainable with caissons. Hence, each of the two methods has its distinct place, the cofferdam in relatively shallow excavations and the caisson in deeper ones. Open cofferdam excavations have been carried down to seventy-five or eighty feet below water, while pneumatic caisson work has been carried down to considerably more than one hundred feet in many cases. Open-well caissons have been sunk even farther. In some of the deeper foundations, temporary sand islands were constructed around the caissons to serve as protection during the progress of construction. The choice of method, cofferdam as against one or other of the forms of caisson, is affected by many factors other than mere depth and the practical ranges of utility of the various systems thus overlap.

The pneumatic caisson is an airtight box with a hollow space on its under side to provide a working chamber. Originally these boxes were built of wood but they are now constructed of steel plates and lined with concrete. When the caisson is in use, the space below is filled with air at sufficient pressure to keep water from passing under the lower edge of the box into the chamber. The inside is thus kept sufficiently dry to permit working directly on the part of the river bed which is exposed within the chamber.

The principle of a caisson is best understood by comparing the device with a drinking glass which is held inverted and, while in this position, is pushed down below water. Through the glass one can readily see that air which has been trapped within it prevents the water from rising more than part of the way. Caissons employ this same principle, the internal pressure being kept high enough to force out under the bottom edge any water which may enter. Air locks are provided to give access to the working chamber by men and materials.

When a caisson is to be sunk through wet soil on land, a hole is first excavated to the ground water level. In this hole the caisson is assembled and excavation begins by undermining its supports to start the sinking operation. If, on the other hand, it has to pass through water into a river bed, any soft mud and similar material is first dredged away from the river bottom to lessen the excavation work that has to be done under air, as well as to give the caisson a start. The steel box, which has been constructed complete or partly complete, is then floated into position, buoyancy for its flotation being provided by the air trapped within the under chamber. Once the box is in position, it is held there by a cribbing of piles to keep it from moving out of place. The trapped air is released and weight is added to the top until the box sinks down into the river bottom; usually this weight is provided by building concrete walls upon

sid
abu
ing
foc

C
tl
o:
ir
E
ir
S

it
tl
sc
tl
tl
w
a:
su
m
cc
h:

it
fc
sc
p:
ca
gc
n
Ii

caisson was the
tions were start

As the box
channel, excava
excavating the
builders workec
the sides. Thr
channel was e
machines, until
own weight dow
The tubes wer
outer wall thre
working cham
pumped dry a
bottom area w
pressed air. Wł
over the entire
with concrete
upon the found

This unique 1
required becaus
no other materi:
a better suppor
rest upon clay,
larger than they
down to rock. .
riprap (large l
outside of each
supporting clay

the caisson and sometimes clay is dumped around the sides to form a seal which helps to keep water from entering the working chamber.

Next, excavation is started within the working chamber and, from time to time, additional weight is added on top to force the caisson farther down into the river bottom as a hole is excavated below it from within. After it has been worked part way into the river bottom, the increased pressure of outside water which results from the greater depth, forces some water into the working chamber. When incoming water becomes sufficient to interfere with work, the chamber is sealed by air locks and compressed-air work begins. While work is being done "under air," the workers enter and leave the lower chamber through these locks, which are simply cylindrical steel rooms each having one door opening into the working chamber and another to the outer air above. Workers enter this chamber through the upper door, which is then closed. The air is brought up to a pressure equalling that of the work chamber below and the lower door can be opened, permitting them to enter the lower chamber. When they are leaving the caisson by means of this air lock, the reverse procedure takes place. Somewhat similar air locks are provided for transferring excavated materials out of the caisson and passing construction supplies to the inside.

As the work of excavation proceeds, removal of this material creates a hole into which the caisson sinks, additional weight above combining to drive it farther into

163

both periodic inspection and proper maintenance to keep it safe.

The long records of our older steel bridges show that they can be kept in good condition with proper care. For example, Brooklyn Bridge is still in daily use by elevated railroad trains, street cars and highway traffic after more than fifty years of service, and it is likely to remain safe for many years to come if present standards of inspection and maintenance are maintained. These require regular examination of all cables, structural steel members and riveted joints; removal of any rust which may have formed; replacement of any parts which show undue corrosion; painting of all steel and iron to protect it from damage by weather; "pointing up" of stone where the mortar is loosening at joints; and repairing or replacing concrete where it shows serious cracks.

Probably most of those who read this book have already observed that a small gap is always left between the ends of rails on railroads of all kinds when tracks are being laid. This is done to allow room for expansion of the steel on a hot midsummer day; without it the tracks would be liable to buckle and thus cause derailments of trains. Indeed, in the earlier days of railroading, this type of accident often happened. When dealing with steel structures of the size of great bridges these allowances for expansion and contraction with temperature changes become surprisingly large. In addition, deflection or bending of the structure and its extension under

176

Fig. 53.—The old Bridge of Heidelberg, built between 1786 and 1788.

FIG. 54.—Wards Island tower, East River crossing of the Triborough Bridge.

FIG. 55.—East River crossing of the Triborough Bridge, Hell Gate Bridge behind.

FIG. 56.—West Bay crossing of the San Francisco-Oakland Bridge under construction.

FIG. 57.—Part of Riverside Drive connections for the George Washington Bridge.

FIG. 58.—Toll booth arrangement, George Washington Bridge.

heavy loads have to be considered also. If no allowance is made for these, some part of the bridge structure is liable to be damaged.

With a temperature range or 110 degrees (about the normal variation from summer to winter extremes at New York City) designers of the George Washington Bridge figured that its steel frame and suspension cables shrink with cold and expand with heat to an extent that, alone, changes the length of the bridge floor between towers by no less than twenty-nine inches. In addition, a further allowance had to be made for movement due to swing and load, which brought the total up to about seventy-eight inches. Hence, expansion joints are provided at each tower to allow for this movement and, instead of being secured at these points, the roadway steel merely rests upon bearings which permit it to slide back and forth. To bridge this gap, which under extreme conditions would attain an opening of *thirty-nine inches,* an ingenious method was used. Where the two adjacent roadway structures meet at a tower, each is provided with a steel grid fashioned much like a giant comb. These grids intermesh with each other and, as the bridge shrinks or expands, their teeth can slide in or out while still providing a gridwork of steel bars to bridge the gap.

Bridge Approaches.

In the early days of bridge building questions of approaches were secondary. This followed from the small

177

amount of traffic usually carried and the fact that horse-drawn vehicles move at low speeds, not requiring roads of the high class that we now build. Generally, a bridge was built with primary regard to having as small spans and as little height as possible, for this simplified construction problems. If, as a result, the roadway had to wind down one hillside and up the other, this was considered a factor of minor consequence.

When railroads came into use, conditions changed, for trains could not run up and down the steep grades that could be traversed by horses. Consequently, railroad bridges were built with primary consideration for the grades of tracks approaching the bridge. Where necessary, the bridge's height, span, and over-all length were increased without hesitation, to permit the use of very gradual inclines for tracks leading to and from it. This was the first departure from old bridge-approach ideas. When the day of the automobile had come, bringing with it a gigantic increase in road traffic, we had to do some very general revising of our ideas as to what a bridge approach should be like. It was no longer enough merely to construct a bridge and assume that existing roadways were adequate. Instead, the entire surrounding areas at each end of an important projected bridge are now studied to ensure that connecting roadways have sufficient capacity to carry the traffic that will be drawn to the new crossing. Designs of the bridge and the connecting roadways are then coordinated to eliminate "bottle-neck" conditions for traffic.

178

As a result of this policy, engineers designing some recent bridges found that it was necessary to make radical changes in the width of adjacent roadways. In other cases they had to cut through entirely new roads to provide adequate approaches, capable of passing the great volume of traffic which the new crossing would attract and could carry. Excellent examples of both old and new methods are found in the cases of certain bridges crossing the rivers that surround Manhattan Island in New York City.

When the old Brooklyn Bridge was built, little was done at first in the way of cutting through new streets or widening existing streets at each end. As one after another of the East River bridges was added, the necessity of approach planning became more and more evident. Elaborate street widening and the creation of some new thoroughfares were found necessary for the Williamsburgh, Queensboro and Manhattan bridges. Even after their completion and their use for some years, still further approach improvements had to be made. It had been found that serious traffic jams resulted from inadequate capacity in the area adjacent to some of these bridges and it took considerable scheming and planning to relieve that congestion. In some cases it was merely alleviated, because it could not be entirely removed. Other cities found the same story to be true when increased numbers of passenger cars and trucks began to appear upon their streets and to make use of their bridges.

179

Profiting by the lessons learned through such experiences, as much consideration is now given to the design of approaches as to the design of a bridge itself. Indeed, the whole work is usually planned as an integral whole. When the George Washington Bridge at New York was designed, spacious plazas were planned, elaborate approaches were devised, and even some new main highways were created to ensure freedom from traffic congestion in approaching the bridge or leaving it. On the New York side, this entailed demolition of a few blocks of buildings to create a plaza, tunneling one approach for several blocks under 178th Street, and constructing some very elaborate connections with Riverside Drive. On the New Jersey side, a large area was devoted to traffic collection and distribution, with numerous small bridges to eliminate grade crossings and delays, while some portions of the new state highways were specially constructed to connect with the bridge plaza. It seems probable that more consideration was given to the design of approaches for this bridge than to those of any previous bridge. As a result, those who use it find that traffic continues moving at a brisk pace even at the busiest time and the traveler is not subjected to the constant and annoying delays so often met with on bridges elsewhere.

Chapter XVI

Erection of Bridges

Erecting Steel Truss Bridges.

A VARIETY of methods have to be used in erecting steel truss bridges, depending upon the size and type of truss as well as upon local conditions and the restrictions which they frequently impose. Small trusses are often completely assembled in the shop and shipped all ready to be lifted into their places, two or more trusses then being secured together to form the bridge. Where trusses are somewhat larger, they may be fabricated in the shop and their parts assembled at the site, either on one bank of the stream or in some other convenient position. From here they are lifted into place and secured together.

Obviously, these methods can be used only for smaller bridges. When trusses are increased to suit the larger structures such handling becomes impracticable and other methods have to be substituted. The commonest method of erecting a large truss bridge is that of making a temporary framework of wood for supporting the structure while under construction. Portions of the truss are then lifted into their positions and they rest upon the temporary falsework while they are riveted or

181

pinned together. After the trusses have thus been assembled, the falsework is removed.

When truss bridges of long span are built, it often becomes necessary to use falsework so elaborate that even this temporary structure becomes, in itself, a rather extensive undertaking. Frequently it is an item of no mean proportions in the construction expense, for it must be strong enough to carry the very considerable weight of a heavy bridge structure which, until completely assembled, is unable to support itself. It often happens that the foundations necessary to support such falsework have to be as large as those required for the permanent support of other bridges of lesser magnitude. This is particularly true when the falsework has to be constructed in a river, a condition generally requiring extensive driving of piles to carry the temporary falsework.

Still other variations are used where conditions favor them. One is the plan of assembling complete bridge spans upon barges, at or near the site, floating the barges into position and then lifting the whole span into its position on the bridge piers or abutments. This method has been used frequently when erecting the suspended span of a cantilever bridge. Since the span has to fit into place between the ends of two cantilever arms, it is quite customary to assemble it upon barges and to lift it into place as a complete unit. In still other cases, the conditions may be such that it is best to use cantilever construction methods. An anchorage system is then pro-

182

vided to tie back the upper portion of the unfinished truss and thus keep the structures from toppling over as they are built out from each pier. In this way erection goes on until both sections meet above the center of the river and are connected to form a continuous structure. Long bridges involving several spans may include more than one type of truss and thus require the application of different methods for each section. Some bridges have been constructed over deep canyons where the height above a gorge prohibited use of falsework and where the builders resorted to other expedients. In such cases, cables strung across the gap have been used to support the structure during erection.

Cantilever Bridges.

One of the important advantages claimed for the cantilever type of design is the fact that no falsework is required for its erection. As mentioned elsewhere, the cantilever structure resembles a pair of brackets, each of which is an arm capable of supporting itself. Since it also supports itself at any stage of progress, this type of construction enables erectors to begin building outwards from each pier towards the center of a span, where the two structures will meet and be connected to form the bridge. In cases where two cantilever arms extend from the same pier, it is not even necessary to provide anchorages sufficient to hold the entire weight, for the builders can work outwards from the two sides of the pier simultaneously, the weight overhanging on

183

each side balancing that on the other. As with truss bridges, the steel framework is fabricated in the shops, carefully fitted so that pieces will assemble together, and then shipped to the site. Erection begins on each of two adjacent piers and as the structures grow outward, the hoisting derricks are moved with them and are supported by the completed portions until these finally meet and are connected together.

Building a Bridge around a Bridge.

In replacing the old Victoria Tubular Bridge over the St. Lawrence at Montreal, in 1898, a unique construction method was used. The old bridge was a single-track structure of the tubular type, closely resembling the Brittania Bridge over Menai Straits, which we described earlier. To meet the demands of increasing traffic, it became necessary to replace this bridge by a larger one, permitting traffic to continue using the old one meanwhile. So a new steel truss bridge was designed to replace the old tubular bridge, in spite of its ability to carry still more of a load than Robert Stephenson, its designer, had intended.

To reduce construction costs, the railroad decided to utilize the identical piers supporting the bridge that was to be replaced. The erectors thus faced a situation calling for some ingenuity, a problem finally solved by the expedient of building the new bridge around the old one before the later was removed. With the old bridge serving as a working platform, new trusses were assembled outside of its tubular structure and not until these new trusses had been completed was the old structure dismantled and taken away.

The method proved so successful that the old Grand Trunk Railway—predecessor of the present Canadian National Railways, as owner of the bridge—continued to operate its trains across the structure during the entire eight-month reconstruction period in 1897 and 1898. So smoothly did all work progress that the bridge was never closed for more than two hours at one time and the total of all periods out of service during the work came to only twenty hours!

Erecting a Steel Arch.

Just which one of several methods may be chosen for erecting a bridge of the steel arch type depends partly upon the size of the arch, although many other factors enter into consideration also. The majority of steel arches are probably constructed by use of cantilever methods. Others have been erected by use of falsework and still others by a combination of cantilever methods and the use of temporary supports. With long-span shallow arches it is not always practicable to hang the whole weight of one half upon tieback cables or bars. Sometimes towers must be constructed to support these tieback cables; in other cases the local conditions are such that tiebacks would involve excessive expense for an anchorage that would be used merely for construction purposes.

185

The Eads Bridge was erected without falsework supports by building the arches out from their piers towards the span centers, the structure supporting itself as a cantilever during the progress of the work. To aid in the support, tiebacks were used, temporary towers being installed on each pier to carry the tiebacks; after completion of the arches both tiebacks and towers were removed. The Hell Gate Bridge was erected without the aid of falsework, cantilever methods again being used with tiebacks carried up to the massive stone towers. Cantilever methods were used also for the Sydney Harbour Bridge, but in this case great cable tiebacks anchored in solid rock were used to hold up the arms as they were branched out from each side to meet over the channel.

When the Bayonne Bridge was erected, groups of piles were driven into the channel bed and temporary steel columns resting upon these were used to support it from below. The structure was then carried out farther, extending as a cantilever beyond each support. These original supports were moved as others were added farther out in the water and the work progressed in this manner until the two structures approaching from opposite sides eventually met and were connected together. Once this connection had been made, the arch became self-supporting and the temporary falsework could be removed. Suspenders were then hung from the steel arch and to these were fastened the heavy steel beams that were to carry the bridge floor.

Erecting a Suspension Bridge.

When a suspension bridge is to be erected, the concrete foundations for towers and anchorages are usually constructed more or less simultaneously. Tower construction follows completion of the foundations and the steel structure, which is generally used nowadays, is fabricated in the shops, shipped in sections and erected in position on its piers. Erection of large towers is accomplished without the use of falsework, a derrick being used to lift the individual sections, columns or braces into position where they can be temporarily bolted together until the riveting gangs fasten them permanently with hot-driven rivets. As the tower structure rises, the derrick is raised with it, the completed portion being used for its support.

In the meantime, while the towers are being erected, the anchorage steel is being set in place and concrete being poured around it to secure it to the anchorage block. Usually this anchorage steel is out of sight, although the upper ends of anchors may be visible in some smaller bridges. In these small suspension bridges the anchorage steel may consist simply of a few steel eyebars with their lower ends securely anchored in the concrete and with attachment holes at the upper ends for fastening the suspension cables or chains. In anchorages of large suspension bridges, there may be required an elaborate grillage of steel beams, buried deep in the concrete, to which are secured several chains of eyebars with only the upper end of the last bar of each chain project-

187

ing above the anchor block. These anchorages must be heavy and strong enough to resist the tremendous pull on the suspension cables or chains which results from their support of the entire bridge. Hence one can readily appreciate how large they have to be for great bridges. In several cases, bridge anchorages have been formed by concrete keys set into large holes drilled in natural rocks at their ends. In most cases they are formed by huge blocks of masonry or concrete, the weight of which is more than sufficient to balance the pull of suspension chains or cables.

With towers and anchorages ready, the next step is that of placing the suspension cables or chains that are to carry the bridge weight. When this work involves merely the construction of a small footbridge, it is a simple matter to lift into position on the tower tops a pair of steel rope cables or chains of steel eyebars, and to secure their ends to the anchorages. In earlier days this was the only method available and even the Menai Straits Bridge chains were lifted into place by man power.

Although unavoidable in earlier years, today this method is usually impracticable because of the large weight which would have to be lifted when constructing a modern suspension bridge. Hence, the suspension system of large bridges is now always built in place, the method depending mainly upon whether cables or chains are used. The practice of "spinning" cables in place was originated by Roebling and one of its earliest applications was on the Brooklyn Bridge. This method has since come into general use for most large bridges, although wire ropes are still used in some cases. Temporary footbridges, carried upon wire ropes and following the curve that will be made by the main cables, are first constructed to serve as working platforms during the erection of those cables. With the footbridges in position, the work of spinning the main cables begins. This term "spinning" is rather misleading to the laymen, for the individual wires which make up the cables are parallel to one another and are not woven as in flexible steel ropes. Such an arrangement is used for several reasons, the chief ones being that parallel wire cables are stronger and stretch less than cables of wire rope.

Each wire is strung into place by means of a traveling sheave which carries a *loop* of wire from one anchorage over both towers and down to the other anchorage. Thus, with each trip of the sheave, two individual wires are strung into place. As the wires are strung they are grouped into strands and as each strand is completed it is laid in its position in the cradle on top of each tower and each end is secured to the anchorage. When all of the strands have been completed in this manner, the whole cable which they form is only approximately round; sometimes it is distinctly hexagonal in shape. In order to form the strands into a round cable, powerful, hydraulically operated "squeezers" are used. These press the whole mass of wires into a circular shape and clamps are then placed around each cable at intervals

189

to hold the suspender ropes which drop from the cables to carry the floor structure. The exposed portions of suspension cables between the clamps are then either coated with heavy grease or painted with a red lead paste and finally wrapped with steel wire to afford external protection.

In the form described, this method was first used in construction the Brooklyn Bridge but it has since become the standard practice in wire-cable suspension systems for large bridges. When the Brooklyn Bridge was being erected, the wrapping wires were applied by hand. Mechanical wrapping devices operated by electric power have since been developed and are now in general use.

Next, suspenders of steel rope are placed in position on the clamps; to the lower ends of these are attached the floor beams or girders which will support the bridge floor when complete. Upon the structure thus formed is built the rest of the floor framework, its arrangement varying according to the design and proposed use of the bridge. If it is being constructed to carry railroad traffic, some type of stiffening truss becomes necessary because of the inherently flexible nature of a suspension bridge. This truss forms the deep framework which can be seen following the contour of the floor on most suspension bridges. Highway bridges do not require as much stiffening as railroad bridges, since the loads of the former are neither so great nor so concentrated and some large highway suspension bridges have practically

no stiffening beyond that incidentally provided by the floor structure itself. Generally speaking, the longer the bridge span, the less is the need of stiffening trusses. This results from long spans requiring such heavy suspension systems that the weight of a single vehicle (or even a train) becomes smaller in proportion to the weight of the large bridge. The George Washington Bridge is the outstanding example of this, its size being such that no stiffening truss is required for roadway traffic. Hence, this bridge has no stiffening truss as yet, although one is to be incorporated whenever the lower deck, with its railroad traffic, is added.

So much for the erection of cable suspension bridges. In the case of chain suspensions, where the main support of the bridge consists of chains of steel eyebars, entirely different methods have to be used. Originally, either of two methods was used: in one the chains were assembled complete on one shore, drawn across the river by means of heavy ropes and thence lifted to the tops of towers. This was the earliest method and was used in the first chain bridges. While sufficient for rather small bridges, it became impracticable when increased size brought with it great increase in the weight of chains. Eventually these larger chains became so heavy that lifting them into place completely assembled was entirely out of the question even by the use of many teams of horses. So a second method was devised. A substantial framework was constructed up to the position and following the contour of the complete chain as it would hang from the

191

towers. We
sembled acr
last pin had
though ten
was cumber
cessive as b
the Florian
the Americ
from tower
bars, strun
the stiffeni
these temp
dispensed
usually da
well to ad
It is one
erected to

Erecting

Erectio
to that of
the fact th
to the pi
upon the
the bridg
proceedin
cantilever
ing assem
taneously
balance a

192

Fig. 60.—Wrapping suspension cables of the Delaware River Bridge.

Fig. 61.—Mechanical screed finishing roadway concrete on the George Washington Bridge.

Fig. 62.—Cable compressors on the George Washington Bridge.

Fig. 63.—Wrapping cables of the San Francisco-Oakland Bridge.

Fig. 64.—Steel erectors seem reckless and almost foolhardy to a casual observer.

Movable bridges of the vertical lift type generally consist of two towers which support the lifting gear, while between them is the movable truss portion. The towers having been erected first, the movable portion of the bridge follows. If there is no objection to temporarily blocking the stream by falsework in the river between these towers, this plan may be used and the movable span erected complete in its position. Since obstruction of the stream usually has to be kept to a minimum of time, the plan most generally used is to erect the movable section upon barges near the site. At some carefully chosen time when conditions of traffic, water level and currents permit, the assembled bridge is floated into the gap between the towers and lifted into place.

Bascule bridges are generally erected by assembling their structural members in place upon the trunnions (or pivots) with the bridge in the "open" position, its frame pointing skywards. There is no necessity of interrupting water traffic until the more or less completed structure is lowered into its level position to permit addition of the roadway, sidewalks and some structural details. Because of the steep angle to which bascule bridges lift, provision usually has to made in the design to obviate the possibility of roadway surfacing sliding out of place when the bridge leaves are lifted.

Cantilever Construction of Vertical Lift Span.

In construction of the Burlington-Bristol highway bridge over the Delaware River, its erectors were faced with a most unusual problem in the 534-foot vertical lift

193

span. At first the intention had been to use the customary method of assembling the span on barges and floating it into place with the aid of tides. However, the risks involved in attempting this with so long a span caused the constructors to substitute a decidedly original method. First, the side span and tower structures were erected practically complete. Then the central, and movable, span followed, each end being built out from its towers as a cantilever towards the center. To hold the heavy structure in position during erection, strong rope tiebacks were carried from connection points of the partly assembled truss up to the top of the respective towers. These ties served to support the partly completed structures until about one-third had been built out from each side. A temporary steel support, resting upon piles in the river, was then placed under the hanging structure on one side of the bridge. This was used as a brace to support the overhang so that erection could be continued until it met and was connected to the portion suspended from the opposite tower.

In the past, all bridge structural members of iron or steel have been pinned or riveted together. So far as possible riveting is done in the shop when the steel is being fabricated; the rest is completed on the job after the members are lifted into position and temporarily held with bolts until the riveters reach that point in the structure. In the past, all riveting has been done with hot rivets, originally by the use of hand hammers and subsequently by pneumatic riveters. Today, much of the shop work is done by "squeezing" the rivets with great pressure instead of heading them by hammer blows. For field work this method has not yet become generally adopted.

The most recent development in bridge fabrication is welding—the fusing together of abutting members by application of heat. This practice began with reconstruction work where bridges had to be strengthened by the addition of new members. Proponents of the method now claim that welds can be made even stronger than the parts which they join. In Germany and other European countries bridges have already been erected in which welding replaced rivets in new bridges; in the United States the practice has not been carried to the same extent. Among some recent all-welded bridge structures is a highway bridge which was built in 1934 across the River Tees in England, the first of its type in that country. In 1933, another welded bridge was built in Japan, this being a short span of the vertical lift type. Two general methods of welding are being used in this type of work: the electric arc and the oxy-acetylene torch. Both names practically explain themselves. The first makes use of the heat of an electric arc, the other that of a torch flame.

Concrete Construction.

As in all other concrete construction, extensive form work is required in building concrete bridges. The piers and abutments are first completed and between them is

195

Bridge foundations, about fourteen deaths and many cases of permanent injury resulted from lack of understanding of the dangers of working under compressed air. However, this problem has been brought under control to such an extent that deaths or serious injuries from caisson disease are now very rare.

Many acts of heroism have been reported in connection with accidents throughout the history of bridge building. In one of its issues of nearly fifty years ago, during construction of the great Forth Bridge, the *Pall Mall Gazette* recorded a story of one of the only too numerous accidents. It seems that staging upon which some men were at work collapsed suddenly, precipitating several to a sudden death on portions of the partially completed steel framework below. Two men were fortunate enough to grasp parts of the structure and remained hanging 200 feet in midair. Efforts at rescue started immediately, but it took some time to climb out along the structure to a point within reach of the pair. As the rescuers finally gained a position from which they could reach one of the men, he called back "Never mind me. I can hold a little longer—go help my mate, he's getting dazed and may drop any moment." It is cheering to be able to report that both men were saved.

Chapter XVII

Superstitions of Bridge Building

Early Human Sacrifices.

AMONG early peoples a certain amount of superstition was always associated with great rivers; often it was the custom to offer them human sacrifices. Even a people so practical as the early Romans were addicted to this belief and we have legends that report their throwing human beings into the Tiber and allowing them to drown as offerings to the stream. The Pons Sublicius—the bridge immortalized in Macaulay's poem about Horatius—was constructed wholly of wood. No iron fastenings were used because it was believed that use of iron would offend the river gods. The opening of this bridge was made the occasion of barbaric religious ceremonies following the custom of the day. A young girl was thrown over the bridge and allowed to drown in the water of the Tiber, while an assembled multitude looked on fervently praying that this sacrifice would appease the gods whose anger they had risked in building the bridge. In other cases we find evidence suggesting that similar sacrifices were made at periodic intervals as part of religious ceremonies.

Upon comparatively recent dates human sacrifices were made to their rivers by the natives of India, who have always been given to this practice in numerous

199

forms. Indeed, the leaning of the inhabitants of India toward human offerings to their gods has often caused a considerable variety of trouble for British authorities, who, since taking over the domination of India, have consistently tried to stamp out the custom. At one time in the earlier days of British occupancy, the engineers found some difficulty in convincing the natives (whose labor was necessary for construction) that the building of bridges over great rivers would not be quickly followed by divine vengeance if a sacrifice were not made in some form or other. Devotees to the practice of human sacrifice seem to have leaned particularly toward the use of young children and infants for this purpose —doubtless because of their inability to protect themselves. Hence, it is not surprising to find records which indicate that some Indian bridges are supported by piers under the foundations of which lie the skulls of little infants, placed there by the fanatical natives in deadly fear lest their river avenge the audacity of the white men in bridging it. In spite of the efforts of the English engineers to eradicate the horrible custom, it seems likely that without their knowledge sacrifices of this kind may have been made and the skulls built into bridge piers as late as the close of the nineteenth century.

A Death Stops the Work.

While the barbarous practice of human sacrifice has finally been relegated to the past even in the most backward countries, there is still much innocent superstition among bridge erectors. Perhaps some of this is due to the risk attendant upon their work of constructing great steel framework to dizzy heights, where the slightest misstep brings certain death. It seems that workers whose daily task involves more than ordinary hazards are notably receptive to superstitious beliefs. Whether working on skyscrapers or bridges, steel erectors may seem reckless and almost foolhardly to a casual observer who sees them walk along the narrow flange of a beam high up in the air. They give him the impression of fearing nothing and their daily task certainly requires a strong heart as well as firm footing. Yet behind all of this front there are certain ingrown superstitions and customs that few of them care to defy. Many a level-headed, hard-hitting, steel erector will spend his full eight-hour day stepping nonchalantly from beam to beam several hundred feet in the air without one thought of danger. But not one of them stays on the job for another minute after some luckless fellow worker misses his footing and comes to a sudden end on the ground below. This, it may be said, is out of respect for the memory of a lost comrade, but it also recognizes the nervous condition of the remaining workers as likely to lead to a second or third loss if the work goes on. Whatever the reason may be, work stops for that day. And with the knowledge that every great structure entails some loss of life, even a hardboiled contractor working against a penalty clause for delay in his contract, never attempts to insist that the workers go on, for he knows too well that his effort would be wasted.

While erecting a tower for one of our recently completed great bridges, some of the steel workers saw a white pigeon circle around and then alight on the upper part of their structure. This, it seems, is considered a bad omen and a few of the men wanted to quit for the day right then and there. However, the scoffings of more skeptical comrades allayed their fears to the extent that they continued, though under protest. But (strangest of coincidences!) just a little later one of their group missed his footing and dropped several hundred feet to the ground below. Immediately all work stopped and every gang made for the construction elevator that was their means of transportation to the base. One can well imagine that some bitter words and not a few curses were aimed at the group of skeptics whose scorn had been the reason for continuing work after the white pigeon alighted on the tower.

Topping the Steelwork.

Steel erectors have an interesting custom which may have had its origin in superstition but is now continued merely to signal an accomplishment. This is the custom of placing their country's flag above a structure when the uppermost piece is put into position. It is a picturesque custom that did not begin with steel but has come down to us from the Dark Ages. The practice goes back so far that no one knows how or when it originated nor what it originally meant. Yet every worker—even though he is building only a small frame house—makes a point of flying the little flag when he puts into place the highest member of his structure. Custom, it seems, permits one variation of the practice. If a flag is not handy a green branch broken from a growing tree can be substituted. It is a quite common sight to see a carpenter, who has just placed the rafters on a small house, reach down and take from his helper a green twig which he proceeds to nail into place on the last rafter. Certainly it is a picturesque custom and, even though meaning but little today, it remains as a reminder of some of the superstitions and customs of bygone ages.

One of the most astounding superstitions connected with bridge building is a belief which is even yet prevalent to some extent among certain elements of the population in South American countries. This is the legend that hard luck always follows the use of any bridge which has been completed without any loss of life! Perhaps it is a lingering relic of the earlier days when human sacrifice was customary. Perhaps it is merely an expression of the feeling that so excellent a record is "too good to be true" and that some more terrible disaster has yet to come. Whatever the basis, it certainly does seem to be an upsidedown superstition. For it would appear more logical to look upon the record as an omen of *good* rather than *bad* fortune, if the contractors finish their work without losing a man. The coldly analytical, scientifically precise, insurance underwriter who is accustomed to weighing and appraising risks would be more likely to interpret it as such.

Caisson Workers' Superstitions.

Workers on the superstructures of bridges are not alone in their leanings toward the whimsies of superstition, for those engaged in the foundation caissons make an equal showing. Before scientific medical study brought to light the cause of caisson disease, this trouble was shrouded in a veil of mystery that made caisson workers a fertile field for superstitious notions. The engineers under whose direction they labored could doubtless have told both interesting and amusing stories about the freakish beliefs that grew out of failure to understand its cause when the first cases of "the bends" appeared. About this time electricity was coming under extensive scientific consideration and a certain amount of general publicity was being given to the work of experiments with what was then a mystic force. Considering this, it is perhaps logical to find that some were inclined to make some vague association between the "bends" and electricity. Only this would seem to offer an explanation of the once-current notion that alternate bands of zinc and silver in contact with the skin of workers would ward off "the bends," for zinc and silver, when in contact with each other and with moisture, give rise to a minute electric current. Whatever the explanation, we know that workers in the Eads Bridge caissons wore bands carrying scales of these metals on their wrists, arms and waists and under the soles of their feet. Just how the notion originated has not been made clear by the writers recording its use, but its complete lack of connection with caisson disease became evident as soon as medical research had definitely determined the cause of the trouble and developed methods for relieving and eliminating it.

We have had man-haters among women and woman-haters among men, but it remained for the compressed-air laborers to create an entirely novel variation of this theme. One of the superstitions which has had more recent vogue among caisson workers is the belief that a death will quickly follow the entrance of any woman into the air chamber! Indeed, this has been carried so far by some that the workers have objected to the mere presence of a woman in the vicinity of the air locks. After this, it is in no wise surprising to find that the prevalent notion associating Friday with hard luck is a firmly seated belief in the minds of some compressed-air workers. Engineers have reported cases where the men have deliberately "stalled" on their jobs and delayed the work for several days just because there was a possibility of their rate of progress making the job ready for air pressure on a Friday. The difficulty in whistling while under air pressure seems to have given rise to still another superstition, for there are caisson workers who consider it the height of folly to tempt evil by whistling in the air chamber!

Chapter XVIII

Bridges of the Future

Greater Bridges Already Possible.

No ONE would dare to predict what bridge builders will attain in size of spans, carrying capacity and other records within the next fifty or one hundred years. Yet, some generalities can be made, for it is evident that coming generations will build bridges still greater than any of those yet erected. This is obvious since only the economics of bridge construction have limited their size to that of the present. We already know that engineers could design and build greater bridges if there were a need for them and we may thus assume that such bridges will follow just as soon as their "need" comes into existence in the form of sufficient traffic to make them economically practicable. Bridge designers have often said that it is "theoretically possible," even with present materials, to build a suspension bridge having a span somewhere between 10,000 and 15,000 feet. But a bridge of that stupendous length would require so much steel to support its own dead weight that the carrying capacity would be reduced to absolutely nothing. Hence, there would be no sense in building it, for great bridges are tremendously expensive structures—

206

far too expensive to build merely for the purpose of establishing a perfectly useless record.

Because it provides an excellent example of what the near future may bring, one new project deserves mention here. This is the "Liberty Bridge" with which it has been proposed to span the entrance to New York harbor, just as the Golden Gate Bridge spans the entrance to San Francisco harbor on the other coast. This project has been advanced with a view to providing a more direct link between Brooklyn and the mainland, by way of the bridges which already connect Staten Island with New Jersey.

The Liberty Bridge is an indication of the next step that is likely to be taken in bridge building, for if this bridge is not built, some other bridge of equal or even greater span will be constructed here or elsewhere at some time in the not-too-distant future. The projected structure would have a span of 4,620 feet, or about 420 feet more than that of the Golden Gate Bridge. The immense proportions of the possible Liberty Bridge may be judged also from the tremendous height of its towers. With their over-all measurements of about 800 feet, they would exceed the height of the sixty-story Woolworth Building, topping it by eight feet! The bridge's two great suspension cables would each be forty-eight inches in diameter, as against the thirty-six-inch diameter of each of the cables of the George Washington Bridge, although the greater number of cables and the larger carrying capacity of the latter bridge would allow it to retain its record for greatest cable strength. As appropriate in a structure to occupy such a dominating position, each of the Liberty towers would have its observation balconies, to be reached by passenger elevators. From these platforms, high above the Narrows, sightseers could look far out to sea, as well as over most of the metropolitan area.

Every Type of Structure Has Its Limit.

Others even greater than the proposed Liberty Bridge may follow, but for every type of bridge there is an ultimate possible limit of size that we cannot exceed. Beyond this, the steel itself would carry down the structure with its own dead weight. Somewhere below this unattainable extreme there is another limit which has been called the "practical limit," since it is the point beyond which size cannot be increased if the bridge is to carry any practical load. Still farther down in the scale we find, for every type of bridge, an economic limit beyond which its construction cost becomes too great and its erection therefore uneconomic. From time to time engineers have estimated these limits for various kinds of bridges but their figures have had to be based upon existing materials and design methods of their day. In consequence, their findings must not be taken for absolute limits as unchangeable as the laws of the Medes and Persians, for improvements in design and the development of lighter or stronger materials will, naturally, shift these limits upward without in the least

208

FIG. 65.—Installing an aluminum floor on Smithfield Street Bridge at Pittsburgh.

affecting the soundness of the reasoning upon which they were based. Therefore, any figures on the limits of bridge spans which engineers can now give us are morally certain to be revised upwards in the future. It is only necessary that we continue our development of stronger materials and introduce some further refinements in our structural designs.

We have already mentioned the possible span of a theoretical suspension bridge incapable of carrying anything more than its own weight. If we consider the necessity of carrying a reasonable load, we find ourselves facing the practical limit. For a suspension bridge this practical limit is now somewhere near 10,000 feet, the figure being governed largely by the individual engineer's interpretation of where a bridge ceases to be practical. The corresponding span limits for cantilever bridges are distinctly lower, the ultimate theoretically possible for a structure carrying merely its own weight being somewhere around 5,000 or 6,000 feet. The practical limit of span for this type is about 3,000 feet and for other types the limits are still lower. But we still have the third type of limit to consider. This is the limit imposed by available traffic, for bridges are not built until their construction cost can be justified. Hence comes an economic limit and we are fairly safe in assuming that the longest existing bridges represent *present* economic limits for their types. Otherwise, still greater bridges would have been built already. This, of course, does not mean that we have reached the end of all progress. As traffic grows, the economic limits will increase and the greater cost of longer bridges will begin to justify itself.

Improvements in Materials and Design Methods.

If we made no advances in the way of improving our designs and construction materials, these growing economic limits would soon bring us up to the practical limits. There we would have to stop, for there could be no greater bridges. But the whole history of engineering has shown that development of designs and materials usually keeps pace with economic demands if, indeed, it does not anticipate them. Hence, it seems likely that we shall further improve both of them before we reach the present practical limits of bridge spans. No one can say just what form improvements will take and we can only look to the past for a clue. Here we find that it has usually taken the form of gradual refinement in structure and gradual increase in the strength of the materials used. Really revolutionary changes in either have been few and far between; most of them turn out to be mere rainbows. Perhaps we may find one answer in the application of some of those very high-strength steels which are used elsewhere in engineering but are yet too brittle, too expensive or not reliable enough for bridges. Perhaps we can find some way of increasing the strength of light alloys of aluminum and magnesium, to permit their use in place of steel. Perhaps still further refinement in structural design might enable us to use our

210

present materials to better advantage and thus push the economic limits upward.

While these thoughts are merely surmise, the past few years have witnessed something which *could* represent the beginning of a new development. This is the application of light aluminum alloys to use in structures. While it is yet much too early to say how far this is likely to go, the innovation has aroused considerable interest among engineers. Aluminum, being only about one-third as heavy as steel, is one of the lightest of metals, and in this lies its promise. Ordinarily its strength is low, that of commercial rolled aluminum being only 25,000 to 40,000 pounds to the square inch in tension. However, certain alloys of the material, and notably those containing 3 to 5 per cent of copper, possess the strength of ordinary steel while still retaining low weight. The utility of these alloys is somewhat impaired by their greater cost in comparison with steel, yet cases have already appeared where this was offset by their advantage of low weight.

An outstanding case was the reconstruction of the old Smithfield Street Bridge, crossing the Monongahela River at Pittsburgh. This bridge was constructed in 1882–1883 after the designs of Gustav Lindenthal and served its purpose well for many years, although becoming inadequate for modern traffic. The first plan was to replace it entirely by a new structure of greater capacity. However, that would have meant closing the bridge for an extensive period—a procedure to which serious objections were raised, since it involved a street-car line which could not be detoured while the construction went on.

A solution was eventually found in the novel plan of decreasing the "dead" weight of the old structure by replacing its steel and wrought-iron floor with a new one of aluminum alloy. In this way, the safe live load could be increased by exactly the amount of weight eliminated through the change.

This idea appealed to the City authorities because it afforded several advantages, not the least of these being the fact that it would cost less than building a new bridge. A curious situation was found here; for the greater cost per pound of the aluminum alloy was more than offset by other savings. Hence, the ultimate total cost would be lowered by its use. Without taking the bridge out of service, one side was closed to traffic and its old floor structure was replaced by a new system of beams, stringers and flooring which was constructed wholly of copper-aluminum alloy. The material used contained from 3.9 to 5 per cent of copper and 0.5 to 1 per cent each of silicon and manganese, while 92 per cent was aluminum. Its tensile strength, in general, ranges from 55,000 to 63,000 pounds per square inch, while the sections used in this work exceeded 60,000 pounds—thus equalling the strength of ordinary structural steel.

This reconstruction resulted in a net saving of about a ton of dead weight per lineal foot, or a total of 800 tons in the length of the bridge. Hence the useful load was increased by the same amount. The new flooring which is carried by these aluminum alloy beams is also made of the same material in the form of channels and angles, with plates to form its upper surface. After the floor structure was placed, this upper surface was spread with asphaltic paving compound which was then rolled smooth with a road roller, leaving about one and a half inches of asphalt to provide the roadway surface.

Future Possibilities of Aluminum.

This first use of aluminum in a bridge structure has been greeted with mixed emotions, some engineers accepting it with open arms and others with very evident skepticism. Certain of its results have already become evident in some of the plans advanced for the reconstruction of other old bridges which require reinforcing, due to their age or to the increased amount of traffic which they now have to carry.

Dr. D. B. Steinman has proposed a plan for reconstructing the floor structure of the old Brooklyn Bridge, using this alloy to permit greater traffic loads by elimination of some of the present dead weight of structure. Incidental to the reconstruction, it is proposed to remove the present diagonal suspenders, to replace the old stiffening trusses with new ones of aluminum and to modernize the structure generally. Through these changes the number of highway lanes would be increased from two to twelve for a total cost of about

$6,000,000, whereas a new bridge providing the same additional capacity would cost about $40,000,000. In all such plans, costs have to be given most careful consideration, since the price (per pound) of fabricated aluminum alloy is several times that of structural steel. However, only about one-third as many pounds are required and, while aluminum is still expensive, the difference is not sufficient to prohibit its use in cases of reconstruction where other savings can be effected.

One can also see possibilities for aluminum in the flooring of some tremendous suspension bridge of the future, where every pound of dead load must be eliminated to make the construction even possible. In developing his design for the proposed Liberty Bridge to span the Narrows at New York, Dr. Steinman found that the substitution of structural aluminum for steel, in the floor framing and wind-bracing chords, would reduce the total cost of the bridge from $40,000,000, to about $35,000,000. Indeed, the Smithfield Street Bridge experiment with its aluminum-asphalt floor might well become historic through pointing the way to the construction of suspension bridges which are now beyond the practical limits of span because of the dead load of their flooring.

It thus appears that all indications point to bigger and longer bridges in the future, since our present limits are mainly those of economics. These economic limits, however, are moving upwards and as still greater bridges are built they may soon reach the more fixed limits of practical span. Perhaps then a trend towards lighter vehicles may help, although this seems more likely to be wholly offset by the greater carrying capacity of these lighter vehicles, if they do come. Again, it is something that only the future can decide. Eventually we shall come to an ultimate limit but when and where this will be is something that we can neither see nor guess at today. The man who dares to put an absolute limit on the span of bridges is likely to find his predictions giving vast amusement to the schoolboys of a generation hence. At least, that is the way that it has worked out in the past. The George Washington Bridge, the San Francisco Bay Crossing or the Golden Gate Bridge would have seemed much more visionary to even Telford or the Stephensons than a one-mile bridge seems to the engineers of today. There is some element of truth in what the professor said when he told his graduating class that "engineers can build anything— *if somebody will pay for it!*"

Index

225